ENGLISH IN ACTION

THIRD EDITION

Workbook 3

ENGLISH IN ACTION

THIRD EDITION

NATIONAL GEOGRAPHIC
LEARNING

BARBARA H. FOLEY
ELIZABETH R. NEBLETT

Australia · Brazil · Mexico · Singapore · United Kingdom · United States

National Geographic Learning,
a Cengage Company

English in Action 3 Workbook, **Third Edition**
Barbara H. Foley and Elizabeth R. Neblett

Publisher: Sherrise Roehr

Executive Editor: Sarah Kenney

Managing Development Editor:
Claudienma Mimó

Senior Development Editor: Lewis Thompson

Associate Development Editor: Katie Davis

Assistant Editor: Becky Long

Media Researcher: Leila Hishmeh

Director of Global Marketing: Ian Martin

Product Marketing Manager: Dalia Bravo

Sr. Director, ELT & World Languages:
Michael Burggren

Production Manager: Daisy Sosa

Content Project Manager: Beth Houston

Manufacturing Customer Account Manager:
Mary Beth Hennebury

Composition: Lumina Datamatics, Inc.

Cover/Text Design: Lisa Trager

Art Director: Brenda Carmichael

Cover Image: © Jean Pierre Lescourret/
Getty Images

For permission to use material from this text or product,
submit all requests online at **cengage.com/permissions**
Further permissions questions can be emailed to
permissionrequest@cengage.com

English in Action 3 Workbook
ISBN: 978-1-337-90600-5

National Geographic Learning
20 Channel Center Street
Boston, MA 02210
USA

Locate your local office at **international.cengage.com/region**

Visit National Geographic Learning online at **NGL.Cengage.com/ELT**
Visit our corporate website at **www.cengage.com**

Printed in the United States of America
Print Number: 04   Print Year: 2022

CONTENTS

THE FIRST WEEK

A Complete each story with the correct verb from the box.

| enroll | got | ~~is~~ | know | meet | studied | study | use |

1. Hi. My name _____is_____ Pierre. I _____ ESL in a part-time program. My classes _____ two days a week from 9:00 a.m. to 12:00 p.m. I already _____ some English because I _____ English in my country for four years. Also, I just _____ a job in a hotel, so I _____ English at work. Next year, I am going to _____ in regular college classes.

| attend | came | didn't study | is | is | speak |

2. Good afternoon. My name _____ Boris. I _____ to the United States two years ago with my son and daughter-in-law. I _____ English in my country, so I _____ an adult school two nights a week. All my friends _____ Russian, so it _____ difficult for me to practice English.

| am | attends | get | is | live | study | talk | works |

3. Hello. My name _____ Mia. I _____ from Tai-wan. My husband _____ for a large international company. We _____ in the United States. I _____ English at a small private school. My daughter _____ public school. I sometimes _____ together with other mothers and we _____ about our children.

B Complete this conversation with the questions from the box.

Do you have any children?	Is your family here?	What kind of music do you like?
How long have you been here?	~~What country are you from?~~	Where do you live?

A: What country are you from? _____

B: I'm from Vietnam.

A: _____

B: I live in Houston, Texas.

A: _____

B: Yes, my whole family is here.

A: _____

B: I've been here for eight years.

A: _____

B: No, I don't have any children. I'm not married.

A: _____

B: I like country music.

C Answer these questions about yourself in complete sentences.

1. What country are you from?

   _____

2. Where do you live?

   _____

3. Where do you go to school?

   _____

4. What are your interests?

   _____

5. How long have you been in the United States?

   _____

6. How many days a week do you study English?

   _____

7. Are you married or single? Do you have any children?

   _____

D Complete the sentences about Fedna and Magda.

1. Fedna and Magda (be) _____ *are* _____ sisters. They (be) _____

   from Haiti.

2. They both (study) _____ English. Fedna (attend) _____

   classes in the morning. Magda (attend) _____ classes at night.

3. Fedna and Magda (work) _____ at the same clothing store, but they

   (have) _____ different schedules.

4. Fedna and Magda (speak) _____ English at work. They also

   (practice) _____ English on their computers.

5. The two sisters (like) _____ sports. Fedna (play) _____

   tennis in the park near her home. Magda (play) _____ basketball at the gym.

E Answer the questions about your school.

| Yes, there is. | Yes, there are. | Yes, they are. | Yes, it is. |
| No, there isn't. | No, there aren't. | No, they aren't. | No, it isn't. |

1. Is your school large? _____

2. Are there many classrooms in your building? _____

3. Is your classroom on the first floor? _____

4. Are there any windows in your classroom? _____

5. Is there a clock in your classroom? _____

6. Is your classroom small? _____

7. Is there a copy machine in your building? _____

8. Is there a computer lab in your school? _____

9. Are there any computers in your classroom? _____

10. Are all the students in your class from the same country? _____

F Look at the picture of the seven sisters. Circle the correct verb in each sentence.

1. All of the sisters **enjoy** / **enjoys** sports.

2. All of the sisters **live** / **lives** at home.

3. One of the girls **are** / **is** on the basketball team at school.

4. None of the girls **play** / **plays** golf.

5. A few of the girls **run** / **runs** in the park in the morning.

6. Some of the girls **go** / **goes** to the gym in the afternoon.

7. All of the girls **like** / **likes** to watch sports on TV.

8. A couple of the girls **want** / **wants** to be gym teachers.

G Complete the sentences about the seven sisters. Use some of the words in the box.

be short	have blond hair	have wavy hair	play baseball
be tall	have long hair	lift weights	play basketball
have a dog	have short hair	~~like to exercise~~	play tennis

1. All of the girls _____ *like to exercise* _____.

2. Some of the girls _____.

3. Many of the girls _____.

4. One of the girls _____.

5. A few of the girls _____.

6. None of the girls _____.

7. A couple of the girls _____.

LISTENING

H Listen and complete the school diagram. 🎧2

ATM	counselor's office	nurse's office	student lounge
bookstore	elevators	~~security desk~~	vending machines
copy machine	men's room	stairs	women's room

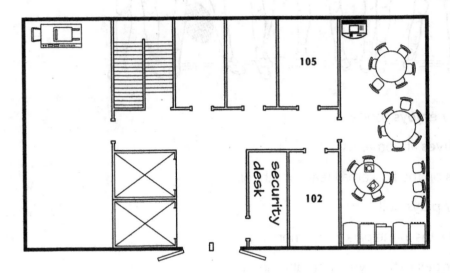

I Listen and write only the true sentences about your school. 🎧3

1. _____
2. _____
3. _____
4. _____
5. _____
6. _____
7. _____

J Listen to each question. Then, circle the letter of the correct response. 🎧4

1. **a.** It's in Room 416. **b.** She's in her office from 1:00 to 2:00.

2. **a.** 12 Broad Street **b.** orange@rccollege.edu

3. **a.** The library is on the first floor. **b.** Show your ID at the library desk.

4. **a.** Yes, it's in Room 318. **b.** All students can use the labs.

5. **a.** Please give me your number. **b.** No, turn off your cellphone before class.

6. **a.** Do pages 34 and 35.   **b.** On Monday

7. **a.** You need to buy two books.   **b.** It's on the first floor.

8. **a.** It's open from 9:00 a.m. to 9:00 p.m.   **b.** You need a library card.

9. **a.** Yes, but we only have one.   **b.** No, I didn't take a vacation.

10. **a.** We finish on June 10th.   **b.** You are expected to attend every class.

11. **a.** Yes, there is a final exam.   **b.** Our first exam is tomorrow.

12. **a.** This is the intermediate class.   **b.** There are four levels.

13. **a.** I hope you feel better.   **b.** Talk to your teacher when you return.

READING   Personal Narrative

The First Day

Raisa leaves work in a hurry, looking at her watch. She usually finishes work at 5:00 p.m., but it is 6:00 already. Today is the first day of school, and her class begins at 7:00. The school is all the way across the city. Raisa is still wearing her green work uniform, but she doesn't have time to go home and change her clothes. There isn't time for dinner either, so she pulls into a fast-food drive-through restaurant. A few minutes later, the traffic stops. There is an accident ahead. Raisa just sits for the next twenty minutes. Finally, the cars start to move again.

Raisa pulls into the school parking lot at 6:55 p.m. and walks quickly to her classroom. The teacher is just closing the door. She smiles and says, "Hi, Raisa." As she walks to the back, looking for a seat, several other students say, "Hi, Raisa." Raisa smiles as she realizes, "Of course they know my name! I'm still wearing my name tag."

Class starts, and the students introduce themselves. Three other students are from Raisa's country, and many other students have been in the United States a long time, too. Some of the other students were stuck in the same traffic jam. After a while, Raisa relaxes. The teacher is friendly, and the class is interesting. Raisa knows it isn't always going to be easy to get to class, but she is glad that she started her English class today. 🎧5

K Answer the questions.

1. Is Raisa's workplace close to her school? _____ No, it isn't. _____

2. Did Raisa work overtime today? _____

3. Why can't she change her clothes? _____

4. Where does Raisa eat her dinner? _____

5. Why is the traffic stopped? _____

6. Is Raisa late for class? _____

7. How do the students know her name? _____

8. Is Raisa new to the United States? _____

LIFE IN THE UNITED STATES

A Circle the correct form of the verb in each sentence.

1. Most Americans **drive** / **drives** to work.

2. The average American **drive** / **drives** to work alone.

3. The average American **don't walk** / **doesn't walk** to work.

4. Many Americans **don't take** / **doesn't take** public transportation to work.

5. Americans **like** / **likes** to spend the evening watching TV shows or movies.

6. Sometimes, American families **eat** / **eats** dinner out.

7. Most American families **have** / **has** barbecues on the Fourth of July.

8. The average American **eat** / **eats** hamburgers, hot dogs, or chicken on the Fourth of July.

9. Most Fourth of July fireworks **come** / **comes** from China.

B Complete the sentences. Write the correct form of the verb in parentheses. Some of the verbs are negative.

1. The average American (live) _____ *lives* _____ in a house.

2. Most Americans (not / live) _____ *don't live* _____ in apartments.

3. The average American (move) _____ many times.

4. Most Americans (move) _____ into larger homes.

5. Most Americans (not / live) _____ in mobile homes.

6. The average American (not / move) _____ for health reasons.

7. I (want) _____ to move to a different climate.

8. I (live) _____ in a two-family house.

9. I (plan) _____ to move this year.

C Look at the graphs and complete the sentences. Use the simple present form of the verbs in parentheses. Some of the verbs are negative.

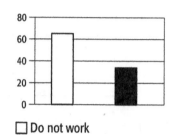

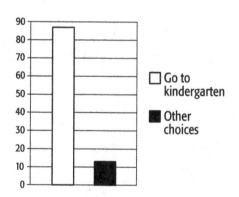

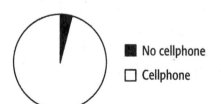

Do you have a computer? (have)

1. The average American _____ has _____ a computer.

2. Around thirteen percent of Americans _____ computers at home.

3. I _____ a computer at home.

4. My classroom _____ computers for the students to use.

Do high school students work? (work)

5. Most high school students _____ during the school year.

6. About thirty-four percent of high school students _____ during the school year.

7. I _____ part time.

8. High school students in my country _____ during the school year.

Do all children go to kindergarten? (go)

9. Most children _____ to kindergarten.

10. The average child _____ to kindergarten.

11. Some children _____ to kindergarten; their parents make other choices for them.

12. Most children in my country _____ to kindergarten.

Do you own a cellphone? (own)

13. The average American _____ a cellphone.

14. Most Americans _____ cellphones.

15. I _____ a cellphone.

16. The members of my family _____ cellphones.

D These sentences are false. To make each sentence true, write the sentences in the negative form. Use *doesn't* and *don't*.

1. The average person sleeps nine hours a night.

   The average person doesn't sleep nine hours a night.

2. Most Americans speak two languages.

   _____

3. The average family has four children.

   _____

4. The average American drinks tea for breakfast.

   _____

5. Most people walk to work.

   _____

6. The average American man exercises every day.

   _____

7. The average worker earns $50,000 a year.

   _____

E Rewrite each sentence. Add the words in parentheses.

1. I am late for class. (never)   *I am never late for class.*

2. They eat out. (every weekend)   _____

3. I take the bus to school. (sometimes) _____

4. We have a test. (every week)   _____

5. I shop online. (sometimes)   _____

6. She eats breakfast. (every morning)   _____

7. He is sick. (hardly ever)   _____

8. They take a vacation. (once a year)   _____

9. We go dancing. (often)   _____

10. My desk is organized. (always)   _____

F Read the chart about the average American woman. Then, complete the sentences using the information from the chart. Some of the sentences are negative.

The Lifestyle of the Average American Woman	Statistics
a. Has a high school diploma	89%
b. Has a college degree	41%
c. Has a full-time job	43%
d. Full-time salary	$40,675
e. Votes in major elections	63%
f. Age at her first marriage	27
g. Volunteers to help others	27%

Source: US Census

1. Most American women (have) _____ *have* _____ high school diplomas.

2. The average American woman (have) _____ a college degree.

3. The average full-time salary for women (be) _____ $40,675.

4. Most American women (earn) _____ more than $50,000 a year.

5. Less than half of the women in the United States (work) _____ full time.

6. The average American woman (vote) _____ in major elections.

7. The average American woman (get) _____ married at 27 years old.

8. Most women (volunteer) _____ in their communities.

G Find and correct the simple present verb mistakes in this paragraph. There are five more.

Every Thursday after work, Angela, Jackie, and Sara ~~goes~~ *go* out to dinner. Every week, the women spends one evening without their husbands or children. They don't talks about problems. They just enjoy an evening out, have a nice dinner, and goes to a movie. Each week, a different person choose the restaurant and the movie. After the movie, at 10:00 or 10:30, the women makes plans for the next week.

LISTENING

H Listen to the statements about each chart. Circle *True* or *False*. 🎧6

How many hours do full-time workers work each week?

1. (True)   False
2. True   False
3. True   False
4. True   False

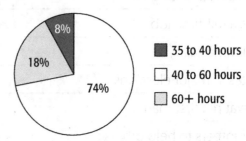

■ 35 to 40 hours
□ 40 to 60 hours
▨ 60+ hours

How many cars does the average American family have?

5. True   False
6. True   False
7. True   False
8. True   False

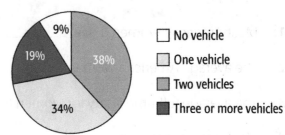

□ No vehicle
▨ One vehicle
▨ Two vehicles
■ Three or more vehicles

I Listen and write the sentences you hear about American workers. Use the words in the box for spelling help. 🎧7

| lunch break   paid vacation   retirement   unions |

1. Eighty-five percent of workers receive health benefits.

2. _____

3. _____

4. _____

5. _____

6. _____

7. _____

8. _____

Homeschooling

Most American children attend public or private schools with other children in a traditional setting. The traditional school has classrooms, a cafeteria, a gym, and other facilities. Today, a growing number of children don't attend traditional schools; they stay at home and participate in homeschooling.

Who chooses homeschooling? The typical family consists of two parents and children, with only one working parent. The other parent stays home and teaches the children what they need to know. Some families join a homeschooling co-op, a group of families that teach their children together.

There are many reasons why parents choose homeschooling for their children. First, some parents think that they can give their children a better education than the local school can. Second, the parents don't like the school curriculum or what the school teaches their children. A third reason is that the parents think that the school's lessons are too easy for their children. Another reason is because of the strong religious beliefs of the family.

The internet is making homeschooling a little easier for parents. Some states, including Florida and Illinois, offer online courses for homeschooled students. Homeschooled students can join classes with other homeschoolers through discussion boards, instant messaging, and video lessons.

Public schools can help homeschooled students. They allow the homeschooled students to participate in after-school activities, such as sports and chorus. Therefore, the students do not miss the social part of school—making friends, talking to classmates, and learning to work with different people. 🎧8

J Read each statement. Circle *T* for *True* or *F* for *False*.

1.	Most American children attend traditional schools.	(T)	F
2.	Homeschooled students eat in school cafeterias.	T	F
3.	A homeschooled child usually has two working parents.	T	F
4.	Parents choose homeschooling because it is cheaper.	T	F
5.	Some parents want to choose what their children learn.	T	F
6.	Some parents with strong religious beliefs prefer homeschooling.	T	F
7.	The internet makes homeschooling easier to do.	T	F
8.	Homeschooled students cannot play sports.	T	F

K What do you think about homeschooling? Write three opinions.

1. _____

2. _____

3. _____

UNIT 3 WORKING AND SAVING

A Sandra attends college full time. Complete the *Yes / No* questions about her college budget. Then, answer the questions.

Expenses	
Tuition	$ 8,000
Books	$ 1,500
Bus	$ 1,200
Clothes	$ 800
Cellphone	$ 1,200
Personal	$ 1,000
Total:	$13,700

Income	
From parents	$ 6,000
Waitress job (Weekends)	$ 5,000
Summer job	$ 3,000
Total:	$14,000

1. _____Does_____ Sandra go to school full time?   _____Yes, she does._____

2. _____ she pay tuition?   _____

3. _____ her parents help her?   _____

4. _____ she pay for her books?   _____

5. _____ her books cost a lot of money?   _____

6. _____ she drive to school?   _____

7. _____ her parents give her $8,000 a year?   _____

8. _____ Sandra work during the week?   _____

9. _____ she have a summer job?   _____

10. _____ her parents want her to succeed?   _____

B Write more *Yes / No* questions about Sandra's budget.

1. _____?

2. _____?

3. _____?

C Put the words in the correct order to write questions about a paycheck.

1. how often / a paycheck / receive / you / do

   How often do you receive a paycheck?

2. money / do / in taxes / how much / you / pay

   _____

3. money / save / how much / every / do / you / week

   _____

4. pay for / does / your company / your medical benefits

   _____

5. receive / electronically / you / your paycheck / do

   _____

D Complete the questions about Liza's schedule.

6:30	Get up
7:00	Walk in the park
7:30	Take a shower
9:00	Get to work
9:00–4:00	Work
5:00	Go to the gym
6:30	Eat dinner
8:00	Watch TV
11:00	Go to bed

1. What time ____does____ Liza ____get up____ ?   At 6:30

2. Where _____ she _____ at 7:00?   To the park

3. _____ she _____ a shower before work?   Yes, she does.

4. What time _____ she _____ to work?   At 9:00

5. How many hours _____ she _____ ?   Seven

6. Where _____ she _____ after work?   To the gym

7. What _____ she _____ after dinner?   She watches TV.

8. What time _____ she _____ to bed?   At 11:00

E Write questions about Stanley's day. Use the words under each picture. Then, use your imagination and answer the questions.

1. How / get to school?
2. What time / get to school?

1. How does Stanley get to school?

   He takes the bus.

2. _____

3. Where / work?
4. How many hours / work?

3. _____

4. _____

5. When / do his homework?
6. How many hours / study?

5. _____

6. _____

7. What time / go to bed?
8. How many hours / sleep?

7. _____

8. _____

F Write two *Who* questions about how each person spends or saves money. Then, answer the questions.

I hate to cook. I eat out every night.
Jay

We save $100 a week. We have $7,000 in the bank.
Carlos and Amy

I work next to a coffee shop. I spend $9 a day on coffee.
Danny

I shop at the mall every weekend. I owe $3,000 on my credit cards.
Gina

1. Who hates to cook? _____ Jay does.

2. Who eats out every night? _____ Jay does.

3. _____ _____

4. _____ _____

5. _____ _____

6. _____ _____

7. _____ _____

8. _____ _____

G Complete the *Yes / No* questions about your class with *Do, Does, Is,* or *Are.* Then, answer the questions.

1. _____Do_____ you attend school five days a week? _____

2. _____ your school in a large city? _____

3. _____ you talkative in class? _____

4. _____ your teacher married? _____

5. _____ your teacher give a lot of homework? _____

6. _____ you always do your homework? _____

7. _____ your class meet in the morning? _____

8. _____ you drive to school? _____

9. _____ you sometimes late for class?   _____

10. _____ this exercise difficult?   _____

11. _____ your school have a bookstore?   _____

12. _____ you bring your dictionary to class?   _____

LISTENING

H Listen. How are these three students paying for college? Circle *True* or *False*. 🎧9

1.	Sam has an athletic scholarship.	(True)	False
2.	Sam has to attend college full time.	True	False
3.	After college, Sam has to pay back his scholarship.	True	False
4.	Katie attends college full time.	True	False
5.	If Katie receives a B, the company will pay for her course.	True	False
6.	If Katie receives a C, the company will pay for her course.	True	False
7.	Oscar needs to borrow $20,000 a year for college.	True	False
8.	After four years, Oscar will owe $80,000 plus interest.	True	False
9.	Oscar is worried about borrowing so much money.	True	False

I Read the answers. Then, listen and write each question next to the correct answer. 🎧10

1. _____   Nine hours a day

2. _____   No, he isn't.

3. _____   Six days a week

4. _____   No, he doesn't.

5. *Where does Tony work?*_____   At Tony's Auto

6. _____   Yes, he is.

7. _____   He's a mechanic.

8. _____   Yes, he does.

College Students and Credit Cards

If you are a college student, you might have a credit card. Fifty-six percent of college students already have credit cards. Older students are more likely to have credit cards than younger students.

In the past, more students had credit cards, but the Credit CARD Act changed that. The Credit CARD Act makes it illegal to give credit cards to anyone under 21 years old unless they have enough income or unless an adult signs up for the credit card with them. The law also stops credit card companies from going to college campuses and offering students gifts for applying for credit cards.

Many college students and their parents aren't sure if credit cards are a good idea. If students pay their credit card bills on time each month, they can build good credit. A good credit score is important for renting a car or an apartment, taking out a loan, and even getting a good job. Also, some credit cards offer rewards like cash back or discounts on travel. On the other hand, if students don't pay their credit card bill in full each month, they will have to pay interest, and their credit card debt will go up. In 2016, 41% of graduating seniors had credit card debt ($3,000 on average). Many students already have thousands of dollars of loan debt from tuition. More instruction on personal finance can help students learn to manage their credit and prevent debt.

Before you get a credit card, ask yourself these questions:

- What is the interest rate? Many companies offer a low rate at first. Then, they increase the rate in six months.
- Is there an annual fee? Some cards have no annual fee. Other companies charge $50 or $100 a year to the card holder.
- What is the fee if I make a late payment?
- Will I have enough money at the end of the month to pay my credit card bill?
- Do I really need a credit card? Maybe a debit card from the bank is a better idea. 🎧11

J Write the correct answers.

1. _____Fifty-six percent_____ of college students have credit cards.

2. The Credit CARD Act does not allow anyone under _____ years old to get a credit card without a good job or help from an adult.

3. _____ of graduating seniors had credit card debt in 2016.

4. The average credit card debt for these students was _____.

K Read each statement. Circle *T* for *True* or *F* for *False*.

1.	All students have credit cards.	T	(F)
2.	Younger students are more likely to have a credit card than older students.	T	F
3.	Credit card companies can go to college campuses.	T	F
4.	Having a credit card can help students build good credit.	T	F
5.	Students need instruction on personal finance.	T	F

THE STATES

A Circle the correct noun in each sentence.

1. Chicago is one of the largest **city / (cities)** in the United States.

2. Many **visitor / visitors** take the city tour.

3. Every **farm / farms** needs a tractor.

4. Death Valley is one of the hottest **desert / deserts** in the United States.

5. There are many **seaport / seaports** on the East Coast.

6. Each **state / states** has a state flag.

7. My cousin lives on one of the Hawaiian **island / islands**.

8. Many big **city / cities** receive a lot of **visitor / visitors**.

9. Every **tourist / tourists** takes photographs of this beautiful park.

10. All of the national **park / parks** are busy in the summer.

B Complete each sentence with the correct form of the verb in parentheses.

1. A glacier (be) _____is_____ a river of frozen ice.

2. A forest (have) _____ many trees.

3. Many large cities (have) _____ seaports.

4. Most mountain ranges (run) _____ from north to south.

5. Farmers in the south (grow) _____ oranges and grapefruit.

6. A valley (be) _____ a low, flat area between mountain ranges.

7. Many tourists (travel) _____ in the summer.

8. A desert (receive) _____ very little rain.

9. Many ships (enter) _____ the seaport every day.

10. Millions of tourists (visit) _____ that city every year.

11. The river (supply) _____ the city's drinking water.

12. The Great Lakes (lie) _____ between Canada and the United States.

C Answer the questions about the map of the United States.

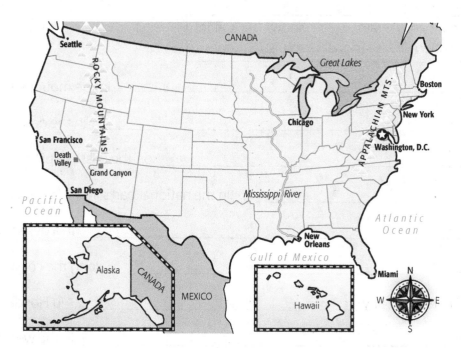

| Yes, there is. | Yes, there are. | Yes, it is. | Yes, they are. |
| No, there isn't. | No, there aren't. | No, it isn't. | No, they aren't. |

1. Are there 50 states in the United States? _____ Yes, there are. _____

2. Is Washington, D.C. the capital? _____

3. Are there six Great Lakes? _____

4. Are the Rocky Mountains in the east? _____

5. Is Hawaii a group of islands? _____

6. Are Alaska and Hawaii separate from the other states? _____

7. Is Hawaii the largest state? _____

8. Is Boston a seaport? _____

9. Are there many seaports on the East Coast? _____

10. Are there many large cities on the coasts? _____

11. Is there a long mountain range in the south? _____

12. Is there a lot of snow in the mountains? _____

13. Is the Mississippi River very long? _____

14. Are there five countries in North America? _____

15. Is Mexico north of the United States? _____

D Complete the sentences with a count or non-count noun from the box.

boats	mountains	rain	~~snow~~	traffic
mountain ranges	pollution	seaports	tourists	trees

1. There is a lot of _____ snow _____ in the mountains.

2. There isn't much _____ in the desert.

3. There are a lot of _____ on the Mississippi River.

4. There are many _____ in the national parks in the summer.

5. There aren't many _____ in a desert.

6. There are many beautiful _____ along the coast.

7. Florida is a flat state. There aren't any _____ in Florida.

8. There are several long _____ in the west.

9. There is a lot of _____ in a large city.

10. The air in the country is clean. There isn't a lot of _____ in the country.

E Complete the sentences with *there is / isn't* or *there are / aren't* and *a lot of, many,* or *much.*

1. The area is very low, so _____ there are a lot of _____ floods.

2. The area receives very little rain, so _____ there isn't much _____ farming.

3. There are many colleges in the city, so _____ bookstores.

4. The city is a major seaport, so _____ boats in the bay.

5. The weather is very hot and dry, so _____ farms.

6. The population of the area is very low, so _____ traffic.

7. The economy is bad, so _____ unemployment.

8. The area is rich in minerals, so _____ mining.

9. The island is rainy and cold, so _____ tourists.

10. There are many immigrants in the city, so _____ ethnic restaurants.

F Read the answers. Then, write questions about North Carolina. Begin each question with *How much* or *How many*.

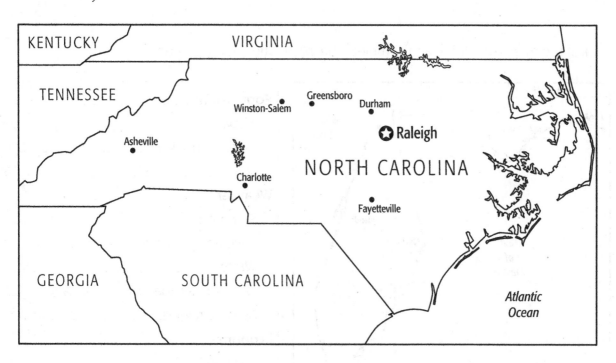

1. <u>How many cities and towns are there in North Carolina?</u>

   There are more than 500 cities and towns in North Carolina.

2. _____

   There are 37 state parks.

3. _____

   There are 75 public universities.

4. _____

   There is a lot of rain, about 50 inches a year.

5. _____

   There is a lot of tourism, especially along the coast and in the mountains.

6. _____

   There are one or two hurricanes in North Carolina every year.

7. _____

   There is a lot of traffic in the large cities.

8. _____

   There are 301 miles of coastline.

9. _____

   There is a lot of farming.

LISTENING

G Look at the map. Then, listen and complete the information about Florida. 🎧12

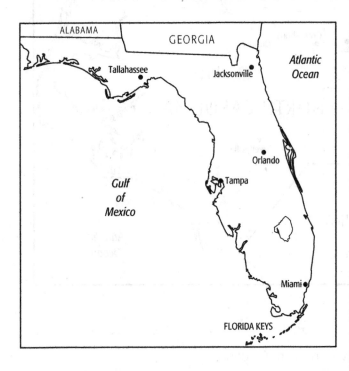

ALABAMA
GEORGIA
Atlantic
Ocean
Tallahassee
Jacksonville
Orlando
Gulf
of
Mexico
Tampa
Miami
FLORIDA KEYS

Population: _____

   Hispanic: _____%

   African-American: _____%

   Senior citizens: _____%

Weather

   Summer: _____

     Average temperature in July: _____°

   Winter: _____

     Average temperature in January: _____°

   Average rainfall: _____ inches

Economy

   Farming: _____

   _____

   Tourism: _____

   _____

H Listen and circle the letter of each correct answer. 🎧13

1. **a.** in the northeast   **b.** in the southwest   **c.** in the southeast

2. **a.** Key West   **b.** the Florida Keys   **c.** Miami

3. **a.** Jacksonville   **b.** Miami   **c.** Tallahassee

4. **a.** 2,984,400   **b.** 20,984,400   **c.** 120,984,400

5. **a.** 16%   **b.** 19%   **c.** 22%

6. **a.** senior citizens   **b.** African-Americans   **c.** Hispanics

7. **a.** the Sunshine State   **b.** the Senior Citizen State   **c.** the Vacation State

8. **a.** 55 inches a year   **b.** 60 inches a year   **c.** 81 inches a year

9. **a.** 55°F   **b.** 60°F   **c.** 81°F

10. **a.** tomatoes   **b.** sugarcane   **c.** oranges

11. **a.** manufacturing   **b.** tourism   **c.** farming

I Listen to the questions about Florida. Then, write short answers. 🎧14

1. _____ No, it isn't. _____   6. _____

2. _____   7. _____

3. _____   8. _____

4. _____   9. _____

5. _____   10. _____

READING   Informational Text

Alaska and Hawaii

Alaska and Hawaii were the last two states to become part of the United States. They are the only two states separated from the continental United States. Alaska became part of the United States on January 3, 1959, and Hawaii joined seven months later on August 21, 1959.

Alaska is located far to the north, separated from the United States by Canada. There is water on three sides of the state. Alaska is the largest state, but it has one of the smallest populations, with only around 739,000 residents. It is also the coldest state: the average winter temperature is 5° Fahrenheit. Millions of people visit Alaska every year to fish in its cold rivers; to see the bears, moose, whales, and other wildlife; and to climb the highest mountain in the country, Denali. Tourism, oil, and fishing are Alaska's major industries.

Hawaii is located in the Pacific Ocean, about 2,400 miles from the West Coast. It is a group of 132 islands, formed by volcanoes millions of years ago. Most of the islands are very small. The majority of the population—around 1,420,000 people—lives on eight main islands. Warm weather and beautiful beaches have made tourism Hawaii's main industry. 🎧15

J Read and check *Alaska* or *Hawaii*. For some statements, both states are correct.

		Alaska	Hawaii
1.	This is the largest state.	☑	☐
2.	This state has a lot of oil.	☐	☐
3.	This state is located in the ocean.	☐	☐
4.	This is the newest state.	☐	☐
5.	This state is warm most of the year.	☐	☐
6.	This state is very cold in the winter.	☐	☐
7.	This state is separated from the continental United States.	☐	☐
8.	Tourism is a major industry in this state.	☐	☐
9.	I would like to visit this state.	☐	☐

A Complete the sentences. Use the present continuous forms of the verbs.

1. Ed and Miranda (plan) _____*are planning*_____
   a trip to Boston.

2. They (not / ask) _____
   a travel agent for help.

3. They (make) _____
   all of the plans by themselves.

4. They (search) _____
   for information online.

5. Patrick (use) _____
   his new phone.

6. He (download) _____
   some new apps.

7. He (learn) _____
   how to use all of the features.

8. He (not / text) _____
   now because he has a lot of homework to do.

9. Gloria (drive) _____
   to work.

10. She (text) _____
    on her cellphone.

11. She (not / wear) _____
    a seat belt.

12. A police officer (follow) _____
    her car!

B Write *Yes / No* questions and answers about the picture. Use the present continuous forms of the verbs.

1. the people / wait / for the bus?

   Are the people waiting for the bus?   Yes, they are.

2. Tomi / check / the bus schedule?

   _____   _____

3. Sophia / read a book?

   _____   _____

4. Jessie / listen to music?

   _____   _____

5. Diti and Chandi / talk?

   _____   _____

6. Roberto / talk on his cellphone?

   _____   _____

7. Mehmet and Lynda / stand in line?

   _____   _____

8. the bus / come soon?

   _____   _____

C Read each answer and complete the question. Use the present continuous.

1. Why <u>is Rosa applying for a loan</u>_____?

   Rosa is applying for a loan because she wants to buy a car.

2. What color sweater _____?

   Gregor is ordering a blue sweater.

3. Which bill _____?

   Joseph is paying the electric bill.

4. Where _____?

   My parents are moving to Texas.

5. Who _____?

   Don is talking on the phone.

6. Which restaurant _____?

   Nelson and Paula are eating at their favorite restaurant.

7. How much money _____?

   Beata is depositing $300 in her bank account.

8. Who _____?

   I'm texting my friend from work.

D Complete the conversation. Use the present continuous.

A: What _____?

B: I'm studying.

A: What _____?

B: I'm studying biology.

A: Why _____?
It's Friday night.

B: I'm studying because I have a test tomorrow.

E Circle the correct verb in each sentence.

1. I **need** / **am needing** a new computer.

2. My sister **belongs** / **is belonging** to the Spanish club at school.

3. **Do you have** / **Are you having** a nice time?

4. I **forget** / **am forgetting** his phone number.

5. They **look** / **are looking** for a new apartment.

6. These cookies **taste** / **are tasting** delicious.

7. Do you feel OK? You **look** / **are looking** sick.

8. The children **love** / **are loving** this movie.

9. I can't concentrate. I **think** / **am thinking** about all my problems.

10. Which **do you prefer** / **are you preferring**, coffee or tea?

F Write the correct forms of the verbs. Use the simple present or the present continuous.

1. Gina usually _____ works _____ on her desktop, but today
   she _____ is working _____ on her laptop. (work)

2. Simon _____ his work every ten minutes.
   He _____ his work now. (save)

3. Mei-Lin _____ her boyfriend an email now.
   She _____ to him about her new job. (write)

4. John _____ the weather for today.
   He _____ the weather every morning. (check)

5. Charles always _____ his bills online.
   He _____ his gas bill now. (pay)

6. Pierre _____ the news from his native country every day.
   He always _____ the political news, news about his
   hometown, and the sports page. (read)

7. Hans _____ English online at this moment.
   He _____ the present continuous. (study)

G Look at the picture. Listen and answer the questions in complete sentences. 🎧 16

1. He's standing in front of the stove. _____
2. _____
3. _____
4. _____
5. _____
6. _____
7. _____
8. _____

H Look at the picture. Listen to the questions and complete the answers. 🎧 17

1. Yes, _____ he is _____. 7. Yes, _____.
2. Yes, _____. 8. Yes, _____.
3. Yes, _____. 9. Yes, _____.
4. Yes, _____. 10. Yes, _____.
5. Yes, _____. 11. Yes, _____.
6. Yes, _____. 12. Yes, _____.

Junk Email

You open your email and find bills, messages from friends or family, important notices, and junk email. You delete the junk email—advertisements, credit card applications, or coupons. You open your email the next day, and there are more messages from the same companies and addresses.

Junk email, which is sometimes called spam, has become a time-consuming headache for computer users. In one day, a person may receive thirty or more junk email messages. Junk email takes up space in your email account. It takes time for you to delete the messages. Some messages may contain viruses that damage your computer.

Junk email is very cheap for the companies or individuals who use it to advertise. They can send thousands of messages per hour. How do these companies get your email address? Every time you order a product online, you are put on the company's email list. When you make a donation online, fill out a form, or just use certain websites, you have to give your email address. Sometimes, companies sell their email lists to other companies.

How can you reduce or prevent junk email? Do not open email messages from people and companies you do not know. Many people install software to block junk email. Many internet providers try to block harmful email so that you never receive it. Most email providers allow you to mark mail from different companies as *Junk* or *Spam*. After you mark one email message as junk, it automatically puts all emails from that company in the junk folder. Remember to empty your junk folder every month.

Sometimes, you can unsubscribe from certain email messages. This means you will no longer receive emails from a particular company or sender. At the end of the email is a message: *Click here to unsubscribe.* If you trust the company, follow the unsubscribe link. If you do not know the company, do not open the email, and do not click *unsubscribe.* Move the email to your junk folder.

Finally, it is very important to read everything carefully when you fill out a form or order a product online. It is often necessary to click a box to keep your name off of a mailing list for advertisers. Click boxes that say, *I do not wish to receive any email* or *You may not share my email address with other companies.* 🎧18

I Answer the questions.

1. Which is **not** an example of junk email?

    a. an advertisement   **b.** a message from your friend   **c.** a travel offer

2. Why is junk email good for companies?

    a. It takes a lot of time.   **b.** It's expensive.   **c.** It's cheap.

3. Read the text again. How many ways can companies get your email address?

_____

4. How can you reduce or prevent junk email?

_____

UNIT 6 A HEALTHY LIFESTYLE

A What suggestions do you have for the health problems below? Write the number of the suggestion under each picture.

1. ~~elevate the leg~~	4. apply lotion	7. stay home from school for a week
2. take cool baths	5. drink tea	8. buy a bandage
3. buy throat lozenges	6. use an ice pack	9. gargle with warm water and salt

chicken pox

Sherri

___ ___ ___

sore throat

Liz

___ ___ ___

sprained ankle

Manuel

1 ___ ___

B Answer the questions about each person in Exercise A in complete sentences.

1. What is Sherri going to do?

   She is going to take cool baths.

2. How long is Sherri going to stay home from school?

   _____

3. What is her mother going to apply to Sherri's face and body?

   _____

4. What is Liz going to drink?

   _____

5. What is Liz going to gargle with?

   _____

6. What is Manuel going to buy?

   _____

7. What is Manuel going to put on his ankle?

   _____

C Answer the questions about Ayumi. She is in bed with the flu and has a temperature of 103°F.

Yes, she does.
No, she doesn't.

Yes, she is.
No, she isn't.

1. Does Ayumi have the flu? _____ *Yes, she does.* _____
2. Is she going to go to work today? _____
3. Is she going to call the doctor? _____
4. Does Ayumi have a fever? _____
5. Does she have a toothache? _____
6. Is she going to take some aspirin? _____
7. Is she going to sleep a lot today? _____
8. Is she going to go to school tonight? _____
9. Does she feel terrible? _____
10. Is she going to drink a lot of fluids? _____

D Complete the questions with the correct words or phrases from the box. You can use some more than once.

How high	How many	What kind of	Which
How long	How much	When	

1. _____ *How long* _____ are you going to be in the hospital?
2. _____ am I going to feel better?
3. _____ stitches is she going to need?
4. _____ specialist are you going to see?
5. _____ pounds is he going to lose?
6. _____ is she going to be in that cast?
7. _____ medicine is he going to need?
8. _____ vaccines are we going to need to travel?
9. _____ is that medical test going to cost?
10. _____ is his temperature?

E Complete the question for each answer.

1. What _____ *is he going to buy* _____ ?

   He's going to buy a bicycle.

2. How often _____ ?

   He's going to ride his bicycle three or four times a week.

3. What kind of food _____ ?

   He's going to cook low-fat food.

4. How many pounds _____ ?

   He's going to lose twenty pounds.

F Complete the conversation.

Kate: Amy! You look wonderful! Congratulations!

Amy: Thank you.

Kate: *When are you due* _____ ?

Amy: I'm due on October 27.

Kate: _____ ?

Amy: We're going to have a boy.

Kate: _____ ?

Amy: We're going to name him Josh.

Kate: I love that name!

_____ ?

Amy: Yes, my husband is going to take two weeks of parental leave.

Kate: _____ ?

Amy: Yes, I am. I'm going to take three months of parental leave.

Kate: _____ ?

Amy: My mom is going to take care of Josh when I go back to work.

G Make predictions about the future with *will* or *won't* and the words below.

1. people / live to be 100 years old

   <u>Most people won't live to be 100 years old.</u>

2. be / a cure for the common cold

   _____

3. people / drive electric cars

   _____

4. every home / have a computer

   _____

5. public transportation / United States / improve

   _____

6. families / have more children

   _____

H Rewrite the sentences. Use *it, him, her,* or *them* for the underlined words.

1. I'll visit <u>Maria</u> in the hospital.   <u>I'll visit her in the hospital.</u>

2. I'll take <u>my mother</u> to the doctor.   _____

3. I'll send <u>flowers</u> to Sandra.   _____

4. I'll take <u>this medication</u> for a week.   _____

5. I'll help <u>my parents</u>.   _____

6. I'll send <u>Jack</u> a get-well card.   _____

7. I'll get <u>your ice pack</u> for you.   _____

8. I'll need <u>these crutches</u> for a week.   _____

9. I'll call <u>my boss</u>.   _____

10. I'll speak to <u>the doctor</u>.   _____

I   You will hear nine sentences. Write each sentence next to the correct picture. 🎧19

1. _____

2. _____

3. _____

4. *The doctor is taking the man's blood pressure.*____

5. _____

6. _____

7. _____

8. _____

9. _____

J   Listen to each conversation. Then, answer the questions. 🎧20

Conversation 1

1.   What kind of a doctor is this woman seeing?   ____*an allergist*____

2.   What is she allergic to?   _____

3.   When does she need the medication?   _____

4.   What shouldn't she eat?   _____

Conversation 2

5.   What is Mr. Jackson's cholesterol level?   _____

6.   How old is Mr. Jackson?   _____

7.   What is Mr. Jackson's prescription for?   _____

8.   What are three causes of Mr. Jackson's medical problems?

_____

K Listen and write short answers about your lifestyle. 🎧 21

1. _____   6. _____
2. _____   7. _____
3. _____   8. _____
4. _____   9. _____
5. _____   10. _____

READING   Informative Narrative

Diabetes

When Diana went for her regular checkup, she told her doctor that she felt tired and that she was always thirsty. Her doctor suggested a blood test for diabetes. The results came back positive. Diana had type 2 diabetes.

Around 29 million people in the United States suffer from type 2 diabetes. In the beginning, the symptoms are often mild. People with diabetes report that they feel tired, are often thirsty, and need to urinate frequently. Diana had many of the common risk factors, too. She was over 45 and had high blood pressure. Diana was 60 pounds overweight, and she did not exercise. Diana is Hispanic, and diabetes is especially high in minority populations, including the African-American, Hispanic, Asian, and Native American communities.

Type 2 diabetes is the most common form of diabetes. In type 2 diabetes, the body does not produce enough insulin or does not use insulin effectively. People with diabetes need to watch their blood sugar levels carefully. In time, diabetes can damage the circulatory system, the nervous system, and major organs of the body. It can cause blindness, kidney disease, and heart disease.

Type 2 diabetes is easy to diagnose with a blood test. It can often be controlled by proper diet and regular exercise. People with diabetes must usually reduce fats and carbohydrates and control their sugar intake.

At first, Diana needed to take diabetes medication. She began to walk and now walks four miles a day. Over the past year, she has lost 50 pounds. Her diabetes is now under control, and she no longer needs to take medication for the disease. 🎧 22

L Read the statements and circle *T* for *True* or *F* for *False*.

1. Many people with diabetes don't know that they have this disease.   Ⓣ   F
2. Most people with type 2 diabetes are under 45 years old.   T   F
3. Type 2 diabetes is more common in minority populations.   T   F
4. Diabetes can damage the kidneys.   T   F
5. A stress test can show if a person has diabetes.   T   F
6. People with diabetes must carefully control their diet.   T   F
7. All people with diabetes must take medication.   T   F

AROUND THE WORLD

A Write the comparative form of the adjectives.

1. The Nile River is (long) _____ *longer than* _____ the Amazon River.

2. Canada is (large) _____ the United States.

3. Dogs are (popular) _____ cats.

4. The Sahara Desert is (large) _____ the Gobi Desert.

5. Texas is (small) _____ Alaska.

6. A firefighter's job is (dangerous) _____ a fisherman's.

7. The Pyramids are (old) _____ the Great Wall of China.

8. Florida weather is (hot) _____ Pennsylvania weather.

9. Are people in your country (talkative) _____ people in the United States?

B Write about the result of each change in the world today. Use *there is* or *there are* and *more, less,* or *fewer*.

1. More people are making their own travel plans, so _____ *there are fewer* _____ travel agencies.

2. Most people buy their music on the internet, so _____ music stores.

3. Many people are ordering items online, so _____ delivery companies.

4. People don't have time to cook, so _____ restaurants.

5. The economy is slow, so _____ unemployment.

6. People are using their phones to take photos, so _____ camera stores.

7. There are more cars every year, so _____ traffic.

8. Most people already have cable TV and internet service, so _____ cable installers.

C Read the information about Austin, Texas and Boston, Massachusetts. Answer the questions about the cities in complete sentences.

Austin, Texas

Boston, Massachusetts

	Austin	**Boston**
Population	947,890	658,279
Average home price	$380,000	$777,024
Sales tax	8.25%	6.25%
Colleges and universities	9	57
Professional sports teams	0	5
Rainy days	88	137
Average high temperature	80°F	59°F

1. Which city is more populated?

   Austin is more populated than Boston.

2. In which city are homes more expensive?

   _____

3. Which city has a higher sales tax?

   _____

4. Which city has more colleges and universities?

   _____

5. Which city has fewer professional sports teams?

   _____

6. Which city has more rainy days?

   _____

7. Which city has warmer weather?

   _____

D Write the superlative form of the adjectives.

1. California redwoods are (tall) _____ the tallest _____ trees in the world.

2. New South China Mall in Dongguan City is (large) _____
    mall in the world.

3. Tokyo has (busy) _____ subway system.

4. The Japanese have (long) _____ life expectancy.

5. California is (populated) _____ state in the United States.

6. In your opinion, what is (beautiful) _____ country in the world?

7. The sun is a star, but it is not (hot) _____ star in the universe.

8. Mercury is (close) _____ planet to the sun and Neptune is

    (far) _____ planet from the sun.

E Complete the sentences using *one of* and the superlative forms of the adjectives in parentheses.

1. Paris, France is _____ one of the most beautiful cities _____ in the world.
    (beautiful city)

2. The Shanghai Public Library is _____ in the world.
    (large library)

3. Mumbai, India is _____ in the world.
    (crowded city)

4. The Louvre is _____ in the world.
    (famous art museum)

5. The Sahara Desert is _____ in the world.
    (hot place)

6. Soccer is _____ in the world.
    (popular sport)

7. The Maltese temple is _____ in the world.
    (old structure)

8. O'Hare is _____ in the world.
    (busy airport)

F Write questions using the words below and *as . . . as*. Then, answer the questions. Give your own opinion.

1. subway train / bus / fast

   Is a subway train as fast as a bus?

   A subway train is faster than a bus.

2. walking / running / good for you

   _____

   _____

3. going to the movies / going to a concert / enjoyable

   _____

   _____

4. police work / military work / dangerous

   _____

   _____

5. living in the city / living in the suburbs / comfortable

   _____

   _____

G Find and correct the mistake in each sentence.

1. Dogs are ^the most popular pets in the United States.

2. Birds are popular in China than in the United States.

3. Computer software is the more popular item to buy on the internet.

4. France is beautiful as Italy.

5. Arizona is sunny than New York.

6. May is not as hot August.

7. This Thai restaurant serves the most spiciest food in town.

8. Denver International is one of busiest airports in the United States.

9. Soccer is more popular then tennis.

LISTENING

H Listen and complete the information about the New York City subway system. 🎧23

Subway system	Year opened	Number of stations	Number of lines	Passengers per day	Cost	Hours open
London Tube	1863	270	11	5,000,000	$6.80 to $8.33	4:45 a.m.–1:00 a.m. 24 hours on Fri. and Sat.
Moscow Metro	1935	206	12	8,200,000	98¢	5:30 a.m.–1:00 a.m.
New York City Subway						

I Look at the chart. Listen and write the name of the correct subway system. 🎧24

1. _London Tube_
2. _____
3. _____
4. _____
5. _____
6. _____
7. _____
8. _____

J Listen and complete the fun facts. 🎧25

1. France has won _the most gold medals_ for Olympic cycling.
2. The people of China drink _____ of water.
3. Walking is _____ in the United States.
4. People in Argentina are _____ consumers of soda.
5. *Avatar* is _____ movies ever made.
6. India produces _____ any other country.
7. Harvard University is _____ in the United States.
8. The Boston Public Library is _____ in the United States.

42 Unit 7

The State Hermitage Museum

The State Hermitage Museum is one of the most famous art museums in the world. It has one of the largest collections. The museum is located in Saint Petersburg, Russia and has five large buildings open to the public. One of these buildings was built in the 18th century as the Winter Palace for Empress Catherine the Great. She collected many works of art. Emperor Nicholas I opened the collection to the public in 1852, and he made the following rules:

1. Everyone had to have a ticket.
2. Visitors had to check their coats, canes, and umbrellas.
3. Visitors were not allowed to touch any of the objects.

His rules were not very different from the rules of museums now. Today, the Hermitage has a few more rules: no smoking, food, pets, or flash photography in the museum.

There are 12 departments at the Hermitage, including the Department of Western European Art and the Oriental Department. A large number of full-time employees work at the Hermitage in addition to many volunteers. A large staff is necessary to take care of the present collection of over three million pieces of art.

One of the oldest libraries in Russia is also a part of the Hermitage Museum. It includes books on art, culture, history, and architecture. It also includes the personal collection of Catherine the Great. Many of the materials are available in European and Asian languages.

The Hermitage is open from 10:30 a.m. to 6 p.m. on Tuesday, Thursday, Saturday, and Sunday and from 10:30 a.m. to 9 p.m. on Wednesday and Friday. It is closed on Mondays and special holidays. About four million people visit the exhibits each year. Admission is around $7.00 for Russian citizens and around $10.00 for all others. However, many visitors can enter for free, including students, veterans of World War II, families with more than three children, and children under the age of 17. 🎧 26

K Scan the reading and complete the chart. How does the Hermitage compare to the other famous art museums? In your notebook, write ten sentences comparing the three museums.

Museum	Year opened	Number of departments	Visitors per year	Cost	Hours open
State Hermitage Museum, St. Petersburg					
Musée du Louvre, Paris	1793	8	7,400,000	$ 18.36	Mon., Thurs., Sat., Sun. 9 a.m.–6 p.m. Wed., Fri. 9 a.m. –9:45 p.m.
Metropolitan Museum of Art, New York	1870	17	7,000,000	$25 Adults $12 Students	Sun.–Thurs. 9:30 a.m.–5:30 p.m. Fri., Sat. 10 a.m.–9 p.m.

MOVING

A Put the verbs in parentheses in the simple past.

Marco and his family (live) _____lived_____ in New York. Marco (be) _____ an assistant manager for a large telephone company. A few months ago, the company (ask) _____ him to move to Ohio because they (need) _____ a bilingual manager for their Cleveland office. His wife (be) _____ unhappy because her family (live) _____ in New York, but she (agree) _____ to move.

When Marco and his family (arrive) _____ in Ohio, they (be) _____ surprised at the cost of houses. Houses (be) _____ much less expensive than in New York! They (look) _____ at many houses. They (like) _____ a three-bedroom home in a small town near Cleveland. They (apply) _____ for a mortgage and only (wait) _____ three weeks for approval. They (move) _____ in last month. They are very happy with the schools and the neighborhood.

B Write sentences to explain how the landlord fixed the apartment before the new tenants moved in. Use the phrases from the box.

call / exterminator	fix	paint	~~repair~~
clean	install / new lock	put in / new carpet	replace

1. The faucet leaked. _____He repaired it._____

2. The carpet was old and dirty. _____

3. The stove was old. _____

4. The air conditioner was broken. _____

5. The kitchen cabinets were dirty. _____

6. The paint in the bedroom was peeling. _____

7. The lock was broken. _____

8. There were ants in the kitchen. _____

C Complete the story. Use the simple past forms of the verbs in the numbered boxes.

1. Paula _____graduated_____ from high school eight years ago.
   She _____found_____ a job in a bakery. She _____ at
   the counter. She (not) _____ in the kitchen.

1. ~~find~~
~~graduate~~
work
work

2. The next year, Paula _____ jobs. She _____ a
   bakery associate. She _____ cakes with flowers and designs.
   She also _____ how to make cookies. Paula liked working in a
   bakery, so she _____ to go to baking school.

2. become
change
decide
decorate
learn

3. After baking school, Paula _____ a job in a different bakery.
   She _____ there for three years and _____
   a lot of experience.

3. find
get
stay

4. Two years ago, Paula _____ a small bakery, Paula's Pies. The
   bakery _____ a big success. People _____ party
   cakes, wedding cakes, bread, and cookies, but her most popular
   items _____ her pies.

4. be
be
open
order

5. Last week, Paula _____. She _____ a much larger
   bakery in town. Every customer _____ a free bag of chocolate
   chip cookies at the grand opening.

5. move
open
receive

D Look at the pictures and answer the questions about Stan's decision to come to the United States.

2016

2017

1. When did Stan get his visa?   _____Stan got his visa in 2016._____

2. When did Stan leave Poland?   _____

3. What city did he fly to?   _____

4. Who met him at the airport?   _____

E Complete the sentences about your childhood with *was / wasn't* or *were / weren't*.

1. My home _____ in the city.

2. My home _____ large.

3. It _____ near a park.

4. It _____ near public transportation.

5. There _____ many good restaurants in my area.

6. There _____ a school nearby.

7. There _____ a lot of children in my neighborhood.

8. The elementary school _____ near my house.

9. My neighbors _____ friendly.

10. My neighbors _____ noisy.

11. My neighborhood _____ safe.

12. My neighborhood _____ busy.

F Write sentences about what you did last night. Use the words below.

1. work: _____ I worked. / I didn't work. _____

2. eat out: _____

3. order a pizza: _____

4. make dinner: _____

5. watch TV: _____

6. do my homework: _____

7. pay the bills: _____

8. read a book: _____

9. call a friend: _____

10. go to bed early: _____

G Complete the story. Use the simple present, future, or simple past.

Time to Move

Last year, Nelson and Helena (decide) _____decided_____ to move to a new apartment. They (like) _____ their old neighborhood, but their apartment (be) _____ too small. They (need) _____ more bedrooms. They (look) _____ for about a month and (find) _____ an apartment in a two-family house near town, but they only (see) _____ the neighborhood during the day, never at night.

Now, Nelson and Helena and their family (live) _____ in the new apartment. They (move) _____ in four months ago. This time, they (love) _____ the apartment. It's on the first floor, and it (have) _____ three bedrooms and two bathrooms. The landlord always (fix) _____ anything that's broken. Last month, Nelson (be) _____ two days late with the rent, but the landlord (not / say) _____ anything.

But, Nelson and Helena (hate) _____ their new neighborhood. In the daytime, it's quiet, but at night, it's a different story. Teenagers (stand) _____ on the street corner and talk loudly. Cars (drive) _____ up and down the street with music playing very loudly. When Helena (come) _____ home at night, she (not / feel) _____ safe walking from the parking lot to the building. Last week, someone (break) _____ into their car and (steal) _____ their laptop. So now, Helena wants to move again, and Nelson (feel) _____ the same way. When their lease ends, they (look) _____ for a new apartment. This time, they (check) _____ out the neighborhood in the daytime and in the evening.

H Listen and complete each answer with a verb in the simple past. 🎧 27

1. She _____came_____ in 2017.

2. He _____ $2,500.

3. I _____ one in Dallas.

4. Her cousins _____ her.

5. He _____ one in a hotel.

6. He _____ with his uncle.

7. He _____ last year.

8. He _____ it two months ago.

9. Yes, he _____ .

10. No, I _____ .

11. I _____ at an adult school.

12. I _____ classes for three years.

13. No, I _____ .

14. I _____ it in September.

15. My sister _____ me.

16. She _____ $4,000.

I Listen to the conversation. Check the correct answer. It is possible to check both *David* and *Maria*. 🎧 28

		David	Maria
1.	Who had a difficult first year in the United States?	✓	☐
2.	Who came to the United States in 2015?	☐	☐
3.	Who studied English before coming to the United States?	☐	☐
4.	Who went to school at night?	☐	☐
5.	Who worked in a parking lot?	☐	☐
6.	Who lived with a friend?	☐	☐
7.	Who had family in the United States?	☐	☐
8.	Who needed a license to work?	☐	☐
9.	Who studied English for four years?	☐	☐
10.	Who do you think had an easier experience?	☐	☐

J Listen to the conversation. Answer each question in a complete sentence. 🎧 29

1. When did Bill and Susan move?

    They moved last weekend.

2. Where did they move to?

    _____

3. Why did they move?

    _____

4. Did Bill want to move?

_____

5. Where did they live before they moved?

_____

6. Why was Susan happy about the move?

_____

7. When is the speaker going to visit his brother and sister-in-law?

_____

READING   Factual Text

The Housing Market

It is the dream of most families—a home of their own. In 2017, 64 percent of families owned their own homes. How affordable is this wish?

A look at the housing market in the United States shows some surprising differences in housing prices. For example, on the West Coast, the median home price is $385,400. In the Midwest, the price is much less, about $283,100. In the South, an average home is $288,900, and in the Northeast, an average home is $483,300. Housing prices are based on supply and demand. How many houses are there? How many people are looking for houses? In areas with strong economies and many high-paying jobs, houses are more expensive. Housing prices near large cities such as San Francisco, Washington, D.C., Boston, and New York are much higher than housing prices in small cities and towns.

The average apartment rental in the United States in 2017 was $1,349 a month. The average monthly payment for a mortgage was $1,494. When interest rates are low, more people buy houses because mortgages are less expensive. When interest rates are high, fewer people buy houses because it is more expensive to buy a house.

How much should a family spend on housing? Banks and lenders recommend that housing costs should be 35 percent or less of a family's monthly income. However, some families are now spending almost 50 percent of their monthly income to have a home of their own. 🎧30

K Read each statement and circle *T* for *True* or *F* for *False*.

1.	Thirty percent of people in the United States own their own homes.	T	(F)
2.	Houses in the Northeast are the most expensive in the United States.	T	F
3.	Home prices throughout the United States are similar.	T	F
4.	Houses on the West Coast are more expensive than houses in the Midwest.	T	F
5.	A house near a city is usually more expensive than a house in a small town.	T	F
6.	It's more expensive to buy a house than to live in an apartment.	T	F
7.	The average apartment rental in the United States is $2,295 a month.	T	F
8.	When interest rates are high, mortgages are less expensive.	T	F
9.	People should spend 35 percent or less of their income on housing.	T	F

NATURAL DISASTERS

A Complete each sentence with *was* or *were*. Then, write the name of the natural disaster that the sentence describes.

| drought   earthquake   flood   forest fire   heat wave   hurricane   ~~snowstorm~~   tornado |

1. There _____was_____ a lot of snow. _____snowstorm_____

2. The temperature _____ over 100 degrees for 20 days. _____

3. It _____ 7.5 on the Richter scale. _____

4. Thousands of acres _____ on fire. The
flames _____ over 100 feet high. _____

5. There _____ no rain for six months. _____

6. The winds _____ over 120 miles an hour. _____

7. There _____ a large, dark funnel cloud in the sky. _____

8. The water _____ ten feet deep. Our house
_____ under water. _____

B Complete each question with *How* and one of the words from the box.

| deep   difficult   far   heavy   long   strong   ~~tall~~   wide |

1. _____How tall_____ are the mountains? They're over 10,000 feet.

2. _____ is the next town? It's about 20 miles away.

3. _____ was the water? It was over our heads.

4. _____ was your test? It was easy!

5. _____ was the box? I couldn't pick it up.

6. _____ was the concert? It was four hours.

7. _____ is the man? He can lift 200 pounds.

8. _____ is your TV screen? It's 52 inches.

When **did** the river **flood**?	It **flooded** in 2016.
Did you **lose** your home?	No, we **didn't.**

C Complete the questions. Use the verbs in the answers to help you.

1. When _____did_____ the storm _____begin_____ ?   It began in the morning.

2. How much snow _____ you _____ ?   We got two feet.

3. _____ you _____ to work?   No, we stayed home.

4. _____ your children _____ in the snow?   Yes, they played outside all day.

5. _____ you _____ your driveway?   Yes, we shoveled for two days!

6. How many tornadoes _____ you _____?   We saw two tornadoes.

7. _____ you _____ any warning?   We had a five-minute warning.

8. Where _____ you _____?   We hid in our basement.

D Complete the questions with *did, was,* or *were.*

1. Where _____was_____ was the flood?

2. How deep _____ the water?

3. _____ you evacuate your house?

4. How _____ you escape?

5. How much damage _____ there?

6. When _____ the hurricane?

7. How strong _____ the winds?

8. _____ you stay in your house?

9. How much damage _____ you have?

10. _____ you scared?

11. When _____ the volcano erupt?

12. _____ you see the eruption?

13. Where _____ you?

14. _____ you lose your home?

15. _____ there any warning of the eruption?

E Put the words in the correct order to write questions about a flood.

1. to rain / begin / it / when / did

When did it begin to rain?

2. it / how many days / rain / did

_____

3. the water / was / how deep

_____

4. you / when / evacuate / did

_____

5. take / with you / did / you / what

_____

6. your house / have / damage / did / a lot of

_____

7. with your friends / stay / did / how long / you

_____

F Write questions to complete the conversation about a storm.

A: *What time did the power go out?*

B: The power went out at five o'clock in the evening.

A: _____

B: I was at home.

A: _____

B: Yes, I had a flashlight. And we lit a lot of candles.

A: _____

B: The power was out all night.

A: _____

B: We ate peanut butter and jelly sandwiches.

A: _____

B: Yes, the water was working.

A: _____

B: I went to bed at nine o'clock.

G Complete the questions about emergency preparedness. Use the simple present, present continuous, future, or simple past.

1. What course _did he take_____?

    He took a course in CPR (cardiopulmonary resuscitation).

2. The family has to evacuate. Where _____?

    They are going to go to the shelter at the elementary school.

3. Where _____?

    She volunteers at the fire station.

4. How much _____?

    She's buying food and water for three days.

5. How many _____?

    She installed four smoke alarms in the house.

6. What _____?

    He's building a safe room under the garage.

7. Who _____?

    The teachers took a first aid course last month.

8. Where _____?

    My family will meet at the hospital in case of an emergency.

9. What number _____?

    He called 911 for emergency help.

10. Where _____?

    We keep emergency supplies in the basement.

11. Where _____?

    Our fire extinguisher is on the wall in the kitchen.

12. Who _____?

    The governor gave the order to evacuate.

13. What _____?

    He's looking for batteries for the flashlight.

14. How quickly _____?

    The fire department responded in five minutes.

H You will hear eight questions about a storm. Write each question next to the correct response. 🎧 31

1. _____ It began at around 6:00 a.m.

2. _____ Yes, they did.

3. _____ Yes, I was an hour late.

4. _____ Yes, there were many trees in the road.

5. _____ It took me two hours.

6. _____ My supervisor couldn't get to work!

7. _How many workers were out?_ _____ About 50 workers were out.

8. _____ No, it wasn't.

I Listen to each question and write the short answer. Use your imagination. 🎧 32

1. _____   7. _____

2. _____   8. _____

3. _____   9. _____

4. _____   10. _____

5. _____   11. _____

6. _____   12. _____

J Listen to the emergency warning on the radio. Write the missing words. 🎧 33

Attention! The National Weather Service has issued a _____tornado_____ warning until

_____ p.m. this evening. A tornado may already be on the ground. Seek shelter

immediately. If you are at home, go into the _____ or the lowest floor. Stay away

from the _____ and _____. Get under a strong _____

and cover yourself with _____ or pillows. If you are in a mobile home,

_____ in your home. If you are in a vehicle, _____ of your vehicle and

lie flat in the nearest ditch or low area.

Hurricanes

Hurricanes are the strongest storms on earth. They bring heavy rain, strong winds, and walls of water from the ocean called *storm surges*. The center of the hurricane is a calm area called the *eye* of the storm. These violent storms have different names in different parts of the world. In the Atlantic Ocean, they are called hurricanes. In the western Pacific, they are called typhoons. In the northern Indian Ocean and Bay of Bengal, they are called cyclones.

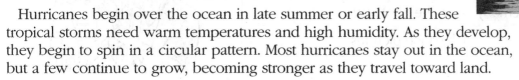

Hurricanes begin over the ocean in late summer or early fall. These tropical storms need warm temperatures and high humidity. As they develop, they begin to spin in a circular pattern. Most hurricanes stay out in the ocean, but a few continue to grow, becoming stronger as they travel toward land.

Weather forecasters follow storms as they develop and travel in the ocean. When the wind speed of a storm reaches 74 miles per hour, it is called a hurricane. Each hurricane receives a name, given in alphabetical order. For example, storm names for 2017 were Arlene, Bret, Cindy, Don, and so on. Hurricanes travel slowly, so weather stations can give residents warnings several days in advance. Hurricanes do not travel in a straight line, so forecasters are not sure at first where a hurricane is going to hit. A *hurricane watch* means that a hurricane may hit in 24 to 36 hours. It is a good idea to buy extra batteries, food, and water and to fill your car with gas. A *hurricane warning* is more definite. A hurricane will probably hit in the next 24 hours. Prepare your property and house. You may need to evacuate.

One of the worst hurricanes in US history hit Galveston, Texas, in 1900. On September 8th, Galveston was a busy seaport of 40,000 residents. By September 9th, half the city was under water and 6,000 people were dead. Hurricane Katrina, in 2005, was the most expensive hurricane. It flooded the city of New Orleans, Louisiana. It caused more than 1,000 deaths and over $80 billion in damage. In both hurricanes, the wind was violent, but the water caused more damage. The storm surges flooded city streets, homes, stores, and buildings. 🎧 34

K Read the statements and circle *T* for *True* or *F* for *False*.

1.	Hurricanes are stronger than tornadoes.	(T)	F
2.	Heavy rain is called a storm surge.	T	F
3.	In some parts of the world, a hurricane is known as a typhoon.	T	F
4.	Hurricanes often occur in the winter.	T	F
5.	All hurricanes cause damage.	T	F
6.	Residents have advance notice of a hurricane.	T	F
7.	A hurricane watch means there is a possibility of a hurricane.	T	F
8.	A hurricane warning is more serious than a hurricane watch.	T	F
9.	Half the population of Galveston, Texas, died in a 1900 hurricane.	T	F
10.	During Hurricane Katrina, the wind caused more damage than the water.	T	F

WEDDING PLANS

A Complete the sentences with *have to* or *has to* and one of the phrases from the box.

~~hold the flowers~~	put a ring on the bride's finger
hold the rings	remain quiet during the ceremony
perform the ceremony	sit in the front row
play good music	take good pictures

1. The bride _____has to_____ _____hold the flowers_____

2. The groom _____ _____

3. The officiator _____ _____

4. The photographer _____ _____

5. The guests _____ _____

6. The best man _____ _____

7. The band _____ _____

8. The parents _____ _____

B Nancy and Nick want to have a simple wedding. They are going to get married at City Hall in a civil ceremony with their parents and a few close friends. They are not going to have a big reception. Circle the correct verb forms.

1. Nancy and Nick **have to** / **don't have to** get a marriage license.

2. Nancy **has to** / **doesn't have to** buy an expensive wedding gown.

3. Nancy and Nick **have to** / **don't have to** bring their IDs to get their marriage license.

4. Nancy and Nick **have to** / **don't have to** invite many guests.

5. Nancy **has to** / **doesn't have to** have a flower girl.

6. Nick **has to** / **doesn't have to** wear a tuxedo.

7. Nancy and Nick **have to** / **don't have to** have a photographer.

8. Nancy and Nick **have to** / **don't have to** send invitations to a lot of guests.

C The Grant family is having their daughter Julia's wedding in the backyard of their home. Mr. and Mrs. Grant, Julia, and Julia's brother, Will, are helping with the preparations. Read their to-do list. Some things are already done. Then, write sentences about their busy week.

Who	Task	Finished
1. Mrs. Grant	go to the supermarket	
2. Mr. Grant	fix the lawnmower	✓ yesterday
3. Julia	pick up her gown	✓ a week ago
4. Mrs. Grant	bake the wedding cake	
5. Will	mow the lawn	✓ yesterday afternoon
6. Mr. Grant	wash the cars	
7. Julia	vacuum downstairs	
8. Mr. and Mrs. Grant	pick up Grandma Grant	✓ two days ago
9. Will	take the dog to the neighbor's	
10. Julia and Mrs. Grant	check with the caterer	✓ yesterday
11. Will and Mr. Grant	set up the tents and chairs	
12. Everyone	decorate the backyard	

1. Mrs. Grant _has to go to the supermarket._

2. Mr. Grant _doesn't have to fix the lawnmower. He fixed it yesterday._

3. Julia _____

4. Mrs. Grant _____

5. Will _____

6. Mr. Grant _____

7. Julia _____

8. Mr. and Mrs. Grant _____

9. Will _____

10. Julia and Mrs. Grant _____

11. Will and Mr. Grant _____

12. Everyone _____

D Write questions and answers about wedding customs in your country. Use *have to* and the words provided. Add extra words when necessary.

1. the groom / ask / the bride's family / for permission / first?

Does the groom have to ask the bride's family for permission first?

No, he doesn't.

2. the families / exchange gifts?

_____

_____

3. the bride / take her husband's name?

_____

_____

4. the couple / exchange rings?

_____

_____

5. the bride's family / pay for / the wedding and reception?

_____

_____

E Complete the sentences so that they are true for you.

has to	have to	had to	doesn't have to	don't have to	didn't have to

1. I _____ take a test to enter this English class.

2. The students _____ pay tuition before this class started.

3. I _____ take this class in the morning.

4. I _____ do homework every day.

5. The teacher _____ take attendance.

6. The students _____ write paragraphs or essays.

7. In my country, students _____ wear uniforms.

8. In my country, the teachers _____ give many tests.

9. In my country, I _____ study a few hours every day.

10. In my country, students _____ study English.

F Read each situation and give your advice. Explain your reasons. Use *should* or *shouldn't*.

> You **should buy** a present from her list. It will be something that she needs for her new apartment.
>
> He **shouldn't arrive** late. He will interrupt the ceremony.

1. Paul works at a company where everyone speaks his native language. Paul is taking English classes twice a week, but no one at his job will practice speaking English with him. What should he do?

   He should find a classmate who also wants to speak English. His classmate will also want to practice.

   _____

   _____

2. Julia needs help. Her apartment is always a mess! There are piles of boxes, books, and papers in all of her rooms. The kitchen table is covered with so many old bills, newspapers, and magazines that she can't use it. What should she do?

   _____

   _____

3. Adrienne and Kenny are getting married in two months. Almost everything is ready. There's one problem—Adrienne's dog, Muffin. Adrienne wants her dog to be part of her wedding ceremony, but Kenny doesn't. The dog is becoming a serious problem. Adrienne says that Muffin is like a family member, and she can't imagine the ceremony without her. What should they do?

   _____

   _____

4. Makiko and Shinjo want to have a small wedding with family and a few close friends. They can't invite all their friends, but they're afraid that some of them will be unhappy if they don't get invitations. What should Makiko and Shinjo do?

   _____

   _____

   _____

G Listen and take notes about what each family member has to do for the trip. 🎧 35

PEDRO
CHRIS
MIKE
RICKY

_____

_____

_____

_____

_____

_____

H Listen to the questions and write the names of the correct family members. You may also write *No one* or *Everyone*. 🎧 36

1. _____Pedro_____ **4.** _____ **7.** _____

2. _____ **5.** _____ **8.** _____

3. _____ **6.** _____ **9.** _____

I Listen and answer the questions. Use *have / has to* or *should* in each answer. 🎧 37

1. They occasionally _____have to stop_____ because it's a long trip.

2. They _____ a cooler because there's a refrigerator in the RV.

3. They _____ because there are many interesting places to see.

4. He _____ any maps because the RV has a GPS.

5. She _____ him because he's only eight.

6. They _____ food for dinner because they're going to eat out.

7. They _____ more than one camera so that more than one person can take pictures.

8. They _____ some games and movies so that the children won't be bored.

A Chinese Wedding

China is a large country and the most populated one in the world. The wedding customs in China vary according to regions. Below is a description of a few typical Chinese wedding customs.

Traditionally, the groom's family has to pay for the wedding reception. They also have to pay for a place for the couple to live. Traditionally, the bride and her family provide the household items: kitchen supplies, bed linens, and furniture. Today, they may even provide the electronic appliances, such as a washer and dryer.

A Chinese bride does not have to wear white. She will often wear red because red is a lucky color in Chinese culture. Today, a modern bride may wear a western-style wedding gown, but she may change into a Chinese-style gown later in the ceremony. The groom usually wears a dark suit.

Chinese wedding ceremonies are often simple. First, the couple must go to a local government office to get a marriage certificate. After they fill out the paperwork, an official checks the forms. Then, they are legally married. Traditionally, the bride and groom do not exchange rings, but today many couples do. The new bride does not have to change her name. She can keep her family's name.

The reception takes place in a hotel, a restaurant, or a wedding hall. Before the reception, the groom must pick up the bride at her family's home. At the family home, the bride's family may play tricks on the groom before they let him take the bride away. Sometimes, the groom gives the family gifts. Then, he will take his bride to the reception in a rented car—often a red one.

Everyone has a good time at the reception. It is a time to celebrate the happiness of the new couple. There is a beautiful banquet with many delicious dishes. A respected older relative will introduce the new couple and make a speech. Then, the couple has to visit each table of guests to receive good wishes from each one. Many of the guests will stand up in front of all the friends and family and express their good wishes for the couple. After the older relatives and friends leave, the young people take over the party. There is music, singing, and dancing. The friends of the couple organize many games for the guests and for the bride and groom. The friends of the bride may play funny tricks on the groom.

The guests give all kinds of practical gifts for the couple's new home. Gifts of money in special red envelopes are also popular. Traditionally, the mothers of the bride and groom each make a quilt for the couple's bed. In the corners of the quilt are four items: dates, peanuts, dried beans, and lotus seeds. They represent the hope that the couple will soon have children, both boys and girls. 🔊38

J Read the questions. Then, number and underline the answers in the passage.

1. What are the differences between a Chinese wedding and a wedding in your native country?

2. Why does a Chinese bride wear red?

3. What happens when the older guests leave?

4. What is the meaning of the four items in the corners of the quilts?

A Match each job with a skill. Then, write sentences with *can*.

1. landscaper	prepare your taxes
2. accountant	solve a crime
3. baker	take your wedding pictures
4. engineer	cash your paycheck
5. bank teller	fill your prescription
6. photographer	make your wedding cake
7. pharmacist	cut your lawn
8. detective	design a bridge

1. A landscaper can cut your lawn.

2. _____

3. _____

4. _____

5. _____

6. _____

7. _____

8. _____

B Write polite requests with *Would you please* or *Could you please*.

1. open the window   _Would you please open the window?_

2. lend me ten dollars   _____

3. give me a ride to work   _____

4. clean the coffee machine   _____

5. take a message   _____

C Complete the sentences about each location. Use *must, must not, can,* or *can't.*

Library

1. You _____must_____ have a library card to check out books.

2. You _____ borrow a book for one month.

3. You _____ write in the books.

4. You _____ borrow books, movies, and CDs.

5. You _____ talk loudly in the library.

Apartment Building

6. Tenants _____ pay their rent by the first of each month.

7. Tenants _____ have dogs, but they _____ have cats.

8. Tenants _____ leave personal items in the hallways.

9. Tenants _____ place their trash in the cans behind the building.

10. Tenants _____ paint their apartments without permission from the landlord.

D Rewrite the sentences. Change *may* or *might* to *maybe.*

1. He might take a vacation. _____Maybe he will take a vacation._____

2. She may get the job. _____

3. I might get a promotion. _____

4. My manager might retire. _____

Rewrite the sentences. Change *maybe* to *may* or *might.*

5. Maybe I will get a raise. _____I might get a raise._____

6. Maybe my company will close. _____

7. Maybe the economy will improve. _____

8. Maybe I will change jobs. _____

E Read each situation. What *may* / *might* happen? Write a sentence with *may* or *might*.

1. Omar often comes to work late. Last week, the boss gave him a warning. He was late again today.

   The boss might fire him.

2. Ivan and his family live in Michigan. His company is moving to Texas. His wife likes Michigan, and his children don't want to leave their friends.

   _____

3. Kaylee bought a coffee maker at Young's Appliances. After one month, it stopped working.

   _____

4. Sandra is at work, but she doesn't feel well. She has a terrible headache.

   _____

5. Jay is a college student. He doesn't know what to major in. He wants to prepare for a career with a good job future.

   _____

6. Beata is a college student. She's majoring in business, but she's having a lot of difficulty in her accounting classes.

   _____

F Circle the correct modals.

1. Lin is at the ticket counter. She **has to** / **should** show her ID to the ticket agent. The ticket agent is telling her that the weather is bad. Her plane **must** / **might** be late.

2. Tory is going through security. He **might** / **must** remove his coat. The red light is blinking. He **might** / **has to** have some change in his pocket. The security screener is asking him, "**Should** / **Could** you please empty your pockets?"

3. The security screener is looking through Leena's baggage. She brought a wrapped present for her sister. She **should** / **has to** open the present for the screener. Also, she packed a bottle of perfume. She **can't** / **doesn't have to** take a large bottle of liquid on the plane. She **has to** / **should** throw it away.

4. It's raining hard. Chad's plane is delayed for two hours. He's worried because he **has to** / **can** attend a meeting in the afternoon. If the rain doesn't stop, he **might** / **should** miss the meeting.

5. Nadia is standing at the baggage claim office. She **can't** / **must not** find her bags. The clerk is telling her that they **should** / **might** be at another airport. She **has to** / **might** fill out a form.

G Complete each conversation with the correct negative modal. Use *must not, can't, (not) have to,* or *shouldn't*.

1. **A:** There's a job opening at the mall.

   B: You _____ shouldn't _____ apply for the job. It's the night shift, and the salary is very low.

2. **A:** Can I wear sandals to work?

   B: No, you _____ wear sandals or high heels.

3. **A:** Do I need to wear a uniform?

   B: You have to wear black pants and a light blue shirt, but you _____ wear a uniform.

4. **A:** What's your schedule?

   B: I work Monday to Friday from 8:00 to 5:00. We're closed on weekends, so I _____ work on Saturday or Sunday.

5. **A:** Where's the employee parking?

   B: Park behind the store. Employees _____ park in front of the store. Those parking spaces are for customers.

6. **A:** How do I look for my job interview?

   B: I like your suit, but you _____ wear so much jewelry. Just wear simple earrings.

H Use modals to complete the sentences about elementary schools in the city where you live now.

1. Children _____ wear uniforms.

2. Young children _____ do many hours of homework.

3. Children in kindergarten _____ study a foreign language.

4. Parents _____ sign their children's report cards.

5. Students _____ pay for their books.

6. Teachers _____ be patient with the students.

7. Children _____ bring cellphones to school.

8. Students _____ attend school during the summer.

9. Students _____ wear shorts to school.

10. Schools _____ conduct fire drills a few times a year.

I Listen and write the sentences next to the correct pictures. 🎧39

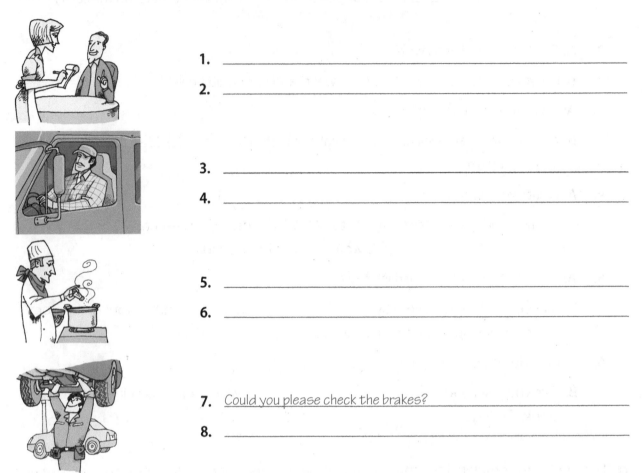

1. _____

2. _____

3. _____

4. _____

5. _____

6. _____

7. _Could you please check the brakes?_ _____

8. _____

J Listen to the conversation between a new cashier in a supermarket and a manager. Read each sentence and circle *T* for *True* or *F* for *False*. 🎧40

1.	The employee is going to attend a training on Monday.	(T)	F
2.	For the training, employees have to wear a red shirt.	T	F
3.	Employees don't have to buy the red shirts.	T	F
4.	Employees can wear sandals.	T	F
5.	Employees must not be late for work.	T	F
6.	Employees must swipe their cards before and after work.	T	F
7.	Employees have to bring a doctor's note when they take a sick day.	T	F
8.	Employees can take a thirty-minute break every four hours.	T	F
9.	Employees can take an hour for lunch or dinner.	T	F

Jobs for the Future

What are the best jobs for the future? Today, service jobs are the fastest growing part of the economy. Many of these jobs have a very good outlook and several can be learned on the job.

As more and more people shop online, truck drivers and delivery workers have a strong job future. Delivery workers pick up items from stores or distribution centers and deliver the products to customers. Delivery drivers make an average of $13.65 an hour. Heavy truck and tractor-trailer drivers transport large shipments across states or across the country. These workers must have a commercial license and a clean driving record. Drivers are often paid by the mile and can earn $19.87 an hour or more.

Solar energy (light and heat from the sun) is being used more and more often in the United States to power homes and businesses. Solar panels collect the sunlight and convert it to electricity or heat. Solar photovoltaic installers (PV installers) put together, install, and repair solar panels on roofs or on the ground. They work outside and also inside when they need to connect the solar panels to the building's electrical system. PV installer jobs are growing faster than average, and the annual salary for these positions is $39,240. To become a PV installer, you usually need a high school degree and about a year of on-the-job training.

Careers in the health fields offer strong future job opportunities. Many of these careers require formal training or education. One medical position that will grow much faster than average is a medical records technician. Medical records technicians organize and manage patient health information, including medical history, test results, and treatment. Technicians must have strong computer skills. Most medical records technicians have an associate's degree or certificate that includes courses in medical terminology, anatomy and physiology, and database systems. Medical records technicians work in doctor's offices, hospitals, and other medical facilities, and their median salary is $38,040.

When choosing a career, consider your skills and abilities and the education necessary. Also, think about the future and ask, "Will that job still be needed in ten years?" 🔊41

K Complete the sentences with the name of one of the jobs from the reading.

1. A _____heavy truck driver_____ must have a commercial driver's license.

2. A _____ has to work outside.

3. A _____ has to have excellent computer skills.

4. A _____ needs a high school degree.

5. A _____ has to have a clean driving record.

6. A _____ must know medical terms.

7. A _____ doesn't have to go to college.

8. A _____ can learn the career on the job.

9. A _____ can earn a good salary.

10. Of these careers, a _____ is the most interesting to me.

UNIT 12 WORKING PARENTS

A Match the two parts of each sentence.

_____d_____ **1.** As soon as the phone rings,

_____ **2.** My son can't watch TV

_____ **3.** When my daughter plays soccer,

_____ **4.** Before I go to work,

_____ **5.** As soon as I get a bill,

_____ **6.** When my son rides his bicycle,

_____ **7.** When Amy gets home from school,

_____ **8.** Before my children go to bed,

_____ **9.** When we go out at night,

_____ **10.** After we have dinner,

a. until he finishes his homework.

b. I drop my son off at school.

c. he wears a helmet.

d. I answer it.

e. my mother babysits.

f. we watch her game.

g. I read them a story.

h. my husband washes the dishes.

i. I pay it.

j. she does her homework.

B Complete the sentences with information about your schedule.

1. As soon as I get up, _____.

2. I _____ after I eat breakfast.

3. I never _____ before I go to school.

4. Before I leave for school, _____.

5. As soon as I get to school, _____.

6. When my English class is over, _____.

7. _____ after I get home from school.

8. I do my homework when _____.

9. After I do my homework, _____.

10. I eat my dinner when _____.

11. I watch TV until _____.

68 Unit 12

C Look at the pictures that show Amy's day. Then, read the sentences and circle *T* for *True* or *F* for *False*.

1.	As soon as she gets up, Amy takes a shower.	T	(F)
2.	Amy takes a shower after she comes home from her walk.	T	F
3.	Before she goes to work, Amy watches TV.	T	F
4.	Amy goes to school before she goes to work.	T	F
5.	When she gets home from school, Amy eats dinner.	T	F
6.	Amy watches TV while she eats dinner.	T	F
7.	After work and school, Amy likes to relax.	T	F
8.	Amy takes a shower before she goes to bed.	T	F

D Complete the sentences about Amy's day with *after*, *before*, *until*, or *when*.

1. Amy takes a walk _____ *after* _____ she gets up.

2. _____ it's raining, Amy doesn't walk.

3. She takes a shower _____ she goes to work.

4. Amy never watches TV _____ she goes to work.

5. Amy goes directly to school _____ she finishes work.

6. _____ she gets home, Amy eats dinner.

7. Amy washes the dishes _____ she finishes dinner.

8. _____ Amy goes to bed, she watches TV or reads a book.

9. Amy watches TV _____ she feels tired.

10. _____ Amy is tired, she goes to bed.

E Read the story. Then, answer the questions. Use a present time clause in each answer.

Mr. and Mrs. Butler have three children—a daughter, Jessica, who is in the eighth grade, and four-year-old twins, David and Joanna. Last year, after 20 years at a telecommunications company, Mr. Butler lost his job. The company downsized, and 1,000 employees were let go. When Mr. Butler lost his job, Mrs. Butler had to go back to work. She's a computer programmer, and now she goes to work five days a week. When there's an important project, she works late at night and even on weekends. Now, Mr. Butler stays home and takes care of the children and the house.

When Mrs. Butler leaves for work, she drops the children off at their schools. Then, she drives to work downtown. When she gets to work, she usually has a cup of coffee and talks with her coworkers. Then, she checks her email and answers her messages. After she answers all her messages, she works on her current projects. When she has a problem, she consults her project supervisor. If she's very busy, she skips lunch or orders a sandwich. When everything goes well, she leaves at 6:00, but if there's a problem, she stays late.

At the same time, Mr. Butler takes care of the home. He's getting used to staying home and taking care of the family.

1. What does Mrs. Butler do when there's an important project?

Mrs. Butler works late when there is an important project.

2. What does Mr. Butler do when his wife is at work?

_____

3. What does Mrs. Butler do before she goes to work?

_____

4. When does Mrs. Butler have a cup of coffee?

_____

5. What does Mrs. Butler do before she works on her current projects?

_____

6. What does Mrs. Butler do when she is too busy for lunch?

_____

7. What time does Mrs. Butler leave work?

_____

F Combine each pair of sentences using the word in parentheses. Change repeated words to pronouns.

1. Mr. Butler finishes the dishes. Mr. Butler does the laundry. (after)

   After Mr. Butler finishes the dishes, he does the laundry.

2. Everyone leaves. Mr. Butler does the dishes. (as soon as)

   _____

3. The twins come home. Mr. Butler reads job ads and sends out resumes. (before)

   _____

4. Mr. Butler makes lunch. Mr. Butler picks up the twins. (after)

   _____

5. Mr. Butler feeds the twins. Mr. Butler and the twins get home. (when)

   _____

6. The twins play in the yard. Mr. Butler calls the twins inside. (until)

   _____

7. Jessica gets home. Mr. Butler helps Jessica with her homework. (when)

   _____

8. Mr. and Mrs. Butler go out for an evening. Jessica babysits the twins. (when)

   _____

9. The family has dinner together. Mrs. Butler gets home at 6:30. (when)

   _____

G Complete. Write the correct pronoun.

1. After my daughter finishes her homework, _____ *she* _____ talks on the phone.

2. When my children get home from school, I'm happy to see _____.

3. When my son finishes school, _____ walks home with his friends.

4. When my children are ready, I walk _____ to school.

5. When my son goes to the park, my husband watches _____.

6. When my daughter has her baby, I'll stay with _____ for two weeks.

7. When I make dinner, the children often help _____.

H Listen to the sentences. Circle the action that happens first. 🎧 42

1. (a.) He reads the newspaper.   **b.** He eats breakfast.

2. **a.** She eats lunch.   **b.** She washes her hands.

3. **a.** I get dressed.   **b.** I listen to the weather report.

4. **a.** She takes a walk.   **b.** She eats dinner.

5. **a.** He has a cup of coffee.   **b.** He eats breakfast.

6. **a.** I get to work.   **b.** I call my husband.

7. **a.** I watch TV.   **b.** I do my homework.

I Listen to Ella talk about her morning routine. Then, answer the questions in complete sentences. 🎧 43

1. What does Ella do when she wakes up?

   When Ella wakes up, she makes her lunch.

2. Does she take a shower before or after the baby wakes up?

   _____

3. When does she eat breakfast?

   _____

4. When does she wake the baby?

   _____

5. When does she give Jesse a bottle?

   _____

6. What does she do after she changes and dresses Jesse?

   _____

7. What does Ella do before she leaves her mother's house?

   _____

J Listen and complete the conversation between a teacher and a parent. 🎧 44

Mr. Jones: Hello, Mr. Reyes. This is Mr. Jones, Daniel's math teacher.

Mr. Reyes: Hi, Mr. Jones. I received your _____ note _____.

Mr. Jones: Yes, I'm concerned about Daniel's _____.

Mr. Reyes: He's having _____ in algebra. Is that right?

Mr. Jones: Yes, Daniel seldom asks for help. He _____ for tutoring.

Mr. Reyes: When _____ tutoring?

Mr. Jones: There is math tutoring every Monday and Wednesday _____.

Mr. Reyes: I _____ with Danny. You will see him every Monday and Wednesday starting _____. Thank you for calling.

READING   Instructive Article

Day Care Centers

In most communities, there are many child care centers, day care centers, and nursery schools. The programs may be similar or very different in terms of their hours, cost, and the ages of children they accept. How can parents decide which program is best for their child?

It is best to visit three or more programs. Look at the facility and the classrooms carefully. Programs should have safe and clean indoor and outdoor play areas. Be sure that the classrooms are bright and attractive. There should be a variety of educational and fun toys, books, equipment, and games. In many classrooms, games and activities are organized in centers. There are sand or water play areas, arts and crafts areas, reading areas with books, rugs, and pillows, an area with blocks and other building materials, and so on.

Ask about the program. Programs for young children should emphasize language skills. There should be songs, stories, games, and the introduction of colors, shapes, and letters. Ask how many teachers and assistants there are in each class. How many children in the program speak your child's language? Do any of the teachers or the assistants speak your child's language? Do you want your child to attend a bilingual program?

It is important for parents to visit the program and observe the classes. The children should be interested and happy. They should know the rules and routines of the class, such as taking turns, putting toys away after playing, and walking—not running—in the classroom.

Start to look and plan early for child care. Some popular programs have a waiting list of a year or longer. In some areas, if you qualify because of low income, the government may help you pay for child care. 🎧45

K Imagine that you are talking to a day care center director. Write five questions you want to ask about the program.

1. _____

2. _____

3. _____

4. _____

5. _____

CRIME

A Look at the pictures and complete the sentences with *before, after, when,* or *as soon as.*

1. _____ After _____ Jill got on the subway, she grabbed a pole.

2. Reggie noticed Jill's large, open purse _____ Jill got on the subway.

3. _____ Reggie did anything, he moved closer to Jill. He noticed that she was wearing headphones.

4. _____ the older woman next to Reggie fell asleep, he took his opportunity.

5. Reggie looked around _____ he reached into her bag.

6. Something bit Reggie _____ he put his hand in Jill's bag. It was her cat!

7. Jill turned _____ she heard Reggie scream.

B Combine the sentences.

1. I opened the door. I turned off the house alarm.

   As soon as I opened the door, I turned off the house alarm.

2. She got into the car. She locked the doors.

   _____

3. He heard a noise. He called the police.

   _____

4. The robber broke into their apartment. They installed new locks.

   _____

5. The shoplifter tried to leave the store. The security guard stopped him.

   _____

C Complete the sentences with the past continuous form of the verbs.

describe	look	play	relax	~~take~~
light	look	read	sit	~~watch~~

1. While the children _____ *were taking* _____ their first

   roller coaster ride, their mother _____ *was watching* _____

   from the ground.

2. My mother and I _____ on the porch

   while my dad and brother _____

   the fire.

3. Yoshiko _____ at a statue while

   Leo _____ information about

   the artist.

4. Monica _____ the sights while her

   friends _____ at everything.

5. While Mr. and Mrs. Walker _____, their

   daughter _____ in the sand.

D Match each time clause with the best main clause.

_____c_____ **1.** While John was running down the hill,

_____ **2.** When I turned on the light,

_____ **3.** While Joan was riding the bus,

_____ **4.** When my car broke down,

_____ **5.** While I was reading a book,

_____ **6.** While the students were taking their exam,

_____ **7.** When I unlocked the door,

_____ **8.** While we were watching the exciting soccer game on TV,

a. our dinner burned.

b. our dog tried to run out of the house.

c. he tripped and hurt his knee.

d. someone stole her wallet.

e. the phone rang.

f. the light bulb exploded.

g. I called for roadside assistance.

h. one student's cellphone rang.

E Complete the sentences. Use your imagination.

1. While I was studying, _____.

2. I was watching TV when _____.

3. The students were talking while _____.

4. The teacher was showing a video while the students _____

_____.

5. I _____ while I was exercising.

6. I _____ while I was listening to music.

7. When I got up this morning, _____.

8. _____ when the students entered the classroom.

9. I was doing my homework when _____.

10. Before I came to school today, _____.

F Write two sentences about each set of pictures. In one sentence, use a simple past clause with *when*. In the other sentence, use a past continuous clause with *while*. Use the verbs under the pictures in your sentences.

read   hear

talk   fall asleep

play   fall

interview   interrupt

sing   bring

1. <u>She was reading a magazine when she heard a noise.</u>

2. <u>While she was reading, she heard a noise.</u>

3.

4.

5.

6.

7.

8.

9.

10.

LISTENING

G Listen and write the words you hear to complete the sentences. 🎧46

1. I _____was walking_____ down the street when I _____ a traffic accident.

2. A man _____ into the intersection when a truck _____ him off.

3. The man in the car _____ his horn when the truck driver suddenly _____.

4. After the truck _____, both drivers _____ of their vehicles.

5. While they _____, a taxi suddenly _____ the back of the car.

6. The taxi driver _____ attention when he _____ the car.

7. Fortunately, a police officer _____ out of a coffee shop when the accident _____.

H Listen to the 911 phone call. Complete the summary of the phone call. You will need to listen to the conversation more than once. 🎧47

Cecilia Roberts _____was coming_____ home from _____.
She _____ into her _____ when she
noticed that the door to her house was _____. She dialed
_____.
The operator _____ her some questions. Cecilia was calling on
her _____. She was parked in the _____
of her home. Then, the operator asked for Cecilia's _____.
Suddenly, the door _____, and someone began coming out of
the _____. At the same time, the operator was trying to get all of
_____'s information. Then, Cecilia noticed that the person who
_____ out of the house was her _____.
Cecilia apologized to the _____.

Jury Duty

Dan Wilson received a **summons** in the mail. The summons required him to report to the courthouse for **jury** duty. He told his employer, and two weeks later, he went to the courthouse. Dan had to be at the courthouse by 8:00 a.m. Before he and the other **jurors** went into the courtroom, they received their name badges and watched a video about jury service. There were 50 jurors that day, so Dan had to wait a long time before they called his number. The **defense attorney**, the lawyer representing the person on trial, selected Dan for the jury, and the **prosecuting attorney**, the lawyer presenting the case against the person on trial, agreed. Not all of the people who were called to jury duty were selected for the trial, so some people were able to go home.

The trial was scheduled for the next day, so Dan was permitted to go home. Before he entered the courthouse the next morning, he turned off his cellphone and put on his juror badge. At 8:30, the jurors went into the courtroom.

Before the trial began, the jurors had to **swear**, or promise, to make their decision according to the law and the **evidence**, or facts. During the trial, both lawyers made statements, showed evidence, and asked questions to witnesses, people who have information about the case. After both lawyers presented their cases, the judge delivered instructions to the jury. She gave the jury information about the laws that were important to the case and reminded the jurors that they needed to follow the laws when they made their decision.

The jury went into the jury room to **deliberate**, or discuss the trial. The jurors elected one person to be the **foreman** of the jury. The foreman led the discussion and counted the votes of the jurors. After the jurors reached a **verdict**, or final decision, the foreman read the verdict to the judge in the courtroom. In the trial that Dan participated in, the verdict was "Not guilty." After the judge accepted the jury's verdict, the person on trial was released, the jury went home, and the trial was finished. 🎧 48

I   Match the two parts of each sentence.

___f___	**1.** A jury	**a.**	is the facts of the trial.
_____	**2.** The prosecuting attorney	**b.**	to listen to all of the evidence at the trial.
_____	**3.** A juror	**c.**	is a final decision.
_____	**4.** A summons	**d.**	in order to reach a decision after all the facts were presented.
_____	**5.** The defense attorney	**e.**	represents a defendant in a trial.
_____	**6.** The jurors had to swear	**f.**	consists of a group of 10 or 12 American citizens.
_____	**7.** The evidence	**g.**	leads the jury discussion about the trial.
_____	**8.** The jurors deliberated	**h.**	is one member of the jury.
_____	**9.** The foreman	**i.**	presents the case against the person on trial.
_____	**10.** A verdict	**j.**	is a written request to report for jury duty.

A Complete the sentences with *before*, *when*, *after*, or *if*.

1. I will get a job _____*after*_____ I graduate.

2. I won't get a full-time job _____ I go to school full time.

3. _____ I finish my classes, I will go straight home.

4. _____ I get stuck in traffic, I will be late for work.

5. _____ I finish the nursing program, I will have to take an important state exam.

6. My supervisor will be angry _____ I make another mistake.

7. I'm going to buy a new suit _____ I go to my interview.

8. _____ I get home from the interview, I'm going to call my best friend.

B Match each time clause with the best main clause.

___*f*___ **1.** If I do well in my biology course,   **a.** I'll have to look for another job.

_____ **2.** After Andrea finishes her courses,   **b.** they will have evaluations.

_____ **3.** Before Steven leaves for his trip,   **c.** many people will lose their jobs.

_____ **4.** After the mall opens,   **d.** his assistant will confirm his flight.

_____ **5.** If the company lays me off,   **e.** it will need more workers.

_____ **6.** Before the employees receive a raise,   **f.** I'll take a chemistry course.

_____ **7.** When the company moves,   **g.** many stores will need salespeople.

_____ **8.** If the company expands,   **h.** she will have an associate degree.

C Look at each picture and use the correct form of *be going to* or *will* to complete each sentence. Use your imagination. There are many possible answers.

1. When her husband comes home, she <u>will take a long, hot bath to relax</u>
   _____.

2. If her husband doesn't come home on time, she <u>will put the children</u>
   <u>to bed early</u>_____.

3. If their neighbors turn down the music, _____
   _____.

4. If their neighbors don't turn down the music, _____
   _____.

5. When the dog's owners come home, _____
   _____.

6. If they don't come home soon, _____
   _____.

7. If the driver has an accident, _____
   _____.

8. If a police officer sees them, _____
   _____.

9. If Mr. Kim passes the eye test, _____
   _____.

10. If he doesn't pass the eye test, _____
    _____.

11. If Ayumi feels better, she _____
    _____.

12. If she doesn't feel better soon, _____
    _____.

D Combine each pair of sentences with a future time clause. Use commas when needed. Change repeated subjects to pronouns.

1. if / it / rain   we / come home / early

    If it rains, we will come home early.

2. before / I / start work   I / check / messages

    _____

3. I / buy / a new car   when / I / get / a new job

    _____

4. if / Bob and Jane / have time   Bob and Jane / go / to the movies

    _____

5. before / John / go to his interview   John / research / the company

    _____

6. Sophia / go back / to college   if / Sophia / lose her job

    _____

7. if / Rick / get a promotion   Rick / be / very pleased

    _____

8. Maria / give away / her winter clothes   Maria / move to Florida

    _____

E Len was a wedding photographer in his native country. He plans to start a photography business in the United States. Read his plans and complete the sentences.

1. Work as a photography assistant; take a few courses in digital photography
2. Buy a top quality camera and printer
3. Develop a business plan
4. Choose a name for the business
5. Advertise the business
6. Hire a photography assistant

1. When Len works as a photography assistant, he _is going to take a few courses in digital photography._
   _____

2. After Len saves some money, he _____
   _____

3. When Len has a good camera, he _____
   _____

4. When Len writes his business plan, he _____
   _____

5. Before he opens, he _____
   _____

6. After Len opens his photography studio, _____
   _____

F Complete the questions.

1. What _____is he going to do_____ after _____he gets_____ to work?
         (he / do)   (he / get)

2. Who _____ if _____ a problem?
       (she / speak to)   (she / have)

3. What _____ when _____ to college?
        (you / study)   (you / go)

4. Where _____ after _____ from school?
         (he / work)   (he / graduate)

5. How many employees _____ when _____
                       (they / hire)   (they / open)
   the new store?

6. What _____ when _____ to your job
        (you / wear)   (you / go)
   interview?

G Edit the sentences. There is one mistake in each sentence.

                                    will take
1. After Jackie talks to her supervisor, she ~~take~~ a few days off.

2. If Jackie's boss didn't give her time off, she will have a problem.

3. When Pierre gets home from work, he always went for a long run in the park.

4. He takes a long shower before he is eating dinner.

5. While Beata was look for her keys, her son found them in the car.

6. Beata called her husband after she was finding her keys.

LISTENING

H Listen to Mr. Miller's job interview. Then, read each question and circle the correct answer. 🎧 49

1. What did Mr. Miller major in?

   a. computer programming   **b.** computer repairs   **c.** computer education

2. How long did he work at his other job?

   a. twenty years   **b.** two years   **c.** two months

3. Why did he leave that job?

   a. He was laid off.   **b.** He was fired.   **c.** He quit.

4. Why doesn't he have a job in computer programming?

   a. He doesn't like computers.

   b. The salaries are high.

   c. The economy is slow.

5. What will he do at the new job? Circle all correct answers.

   a. He will repair computers.   **c.** He will teach computer classes.

   b. He will sell computers.   **d.** He will answer questions at a help desk.

6. If his sales are good, he will . . .

   a. earn $50 an hour.

   b. earn a ten percent commission.

   c. earn more money after six months.

7. Mr. Miller will receive a phone call . . .

   a. if he likes the job.   **b.** if he gets the job.   **c.** if a class is available.

I Listen and circle the correct main clause. 🎧 50

1. **a.** . . . I locked it.   **b.** . . . I opened it.

2. **a.** . . . she writes it.   **b.** . . . she'll go to the bank.

3. **a.** . . . he leaves work.   **b.** . . . he will help his kids with their homework.

4. **a.** . . . Mia will relax.   **b.** . . . Mia asked questions.

5. **a.** . . . she will arrive at the office.   **b.** . . . she put on her uniform.

6. **a.** . . . he'll take a sick day from work.   **b.** . . . he'll get sick.

Travel Nurses

Nursing is the largest healthcare profession in the United States. There were 2,955,200 nurses employed in 2016, and by 2026 there will be around 3,400,000. However, there is still a need for nurses. In the US, there are hundreds of thousands of job openings for nurses each year. Many hospitals and healthcare facilities need temporary nurses to cover for full-time staff and to assist during busy seasons. Travel nurses can help at these times.

Travel nurses work at hospitals and healthcare facilities for short lengths of time, usually four to thirteen weeks. These nurses can choose where they work and for how long through the agencies that hire them for temporary jobs. Travel nurses can take jobs near where they live or anywhere around the country. The agencies often provide healthcare benefits, paid time off, and free furnished housing while the nurses are working. Also, the agencies usually pay for the nurses to travel to and from their job assignments.

Many travel nurses choose this type of nursing because they enjoy living in new places and working in many different locations. They can work with different kinds of patients and in different healthcare facilities. Travel nurses may receive higher pay than nurses who work full-time at one hospital. Also, travel nurses have guaranteed hours, so they know exactly how many hours they will work each week, and they receive higher pay for overtime work (anything over 40 hours a week).

There are a number of requirements to become a travel nurse. First, a person needs at least one year of experience as a registered nurse. Second, the applicant needs a nursing license for the state where he or she wants to work. This can be complicated because many states require a test and an application for a license to work in that state. However, the agencies will often pay for some of the costs of getting a license. Finally, some specialties, like emergency room nursing or pediatric nursing, may require more training. Being a travel nurse is a great career option for a person who likes to travel and wants to work in different hospitals throughout the country. 🎧51

J   Read the statements and circle *T* for *True* or *F* for *False*.

1.	There are many job openings for nurses.	Ⓣ	F
2.	Travel nurses can help when hospitals need more nurses during busy seasons.	T	F
3.	Travel nurses work for two weeks at a time.	T	F
4.	Agencies often give nurses health insurance.	T	F
5.	Travel nurses get paid less than full-time nurses.	T	F
6.	Travel nurses get paid extra for overtime work.	T	F
7.	You need five years of experience to be a travel nurse.	T	F
8.	Travel nurses need nursing licenses for all 50 states.	T	F

SPELLING RULES

Plural Nouns

1. For most nouns, add -s.
   boy – boys   store – stores   student – students

2. If a noun ends with a consonant and a *y*, change the *y* to *i*, and add -es.
   city – cities   dictionary – dictionaries   baby – babies

3. If a noun ends with *sh*, *ch*, *x*, or *z*, add -es.
   box – boxes   dress – dresses   watch – watches

Present Continuous Verbs

1. For most verbs, add -ing.
   walk – walking   play – playing   eat – eating

2. If a verb ends in *e*, drop the *e* and add -ing.
   write – writing   come – coming   drive – driving

3. If a verb ends in a consonant + vowel + consonant, double the final consonant and add -ing.
   sit – sitting   run – running   put – putting

Present: Third Person

1. For most verbs, add -s.
   make – makes   call – calls   sleep – sleeps

2. If a verb ends with a consonant and a *y*, change the *y* to *i*, and add -es.
   try – tries   cry – cries   apply – applies

3. If a verb ends with *sh*, *ch*, *x*, or *z*, add -es.
   wash – washes   watch – watches   fix – fixes

4. These verbs are irregular in the third person.
   have – has   do – does

Past Verbs

1. For most verbs, add -d or -ed.
   save – saved   *rent – rented*

2. If a verb ends in a consonant + y, change the y to i and add -ed.
   try – tried   *study – studied*

3. If a verb ends in a consonant + vowel + consonant, double the final consonant and add -ed.
   stop – stopped   *rob – robbed*

4. If a verb ends in w, x, or y, do not double the consonant. Add -ed.
   play – played   *relax – relaxed*   *snow – snowed*

Comparative Adjectives: -er

1. For most adjectives, add -r or -er.
   cold – colder   *short – shorter*   *tall – taller*

2. If a one-syllable adjective ends in a consonant + vowel + consonant, double the final consonant and add -er.
   big – bigger   *thin – thinner*   *sad – sadder*

3. If an adjective ends in a consonant + y, change the y to i and add -er.
   happy – happier   *heavy – heavier*   *friendly – friendlier*

IRREGULAR PAST VERBS

Present	Past	Present	Past	Present	Past	Present	Past
be	was, were	fall	fell	lose	lost	speak	spoke
begin	began	feel	felt	make	made	spend	spent
break	broke	find	found	meet	met	stand	stood
bring	brought	fly	flew	pay	paid	take	took
build	built	forget	forgot	put	put	teach	taught
buy	bought	get	got	read	read	tell	told
come	came	give	gave	run	ran	think	thought
cost	cost	go	went	say	said	understand	understood
cut	cut	grow	grew	see	saw	wake	woke
do	did	have	had	send	sent	wear	wore
drink	drank	hear	heard	sing	sang	win	won
drive	drove	know	knew	sit	sat	write	wrote
eat	ate	leave	left	sleep	slept		

CREDITS